Unit Tests for Progress Monitoring

D1500946

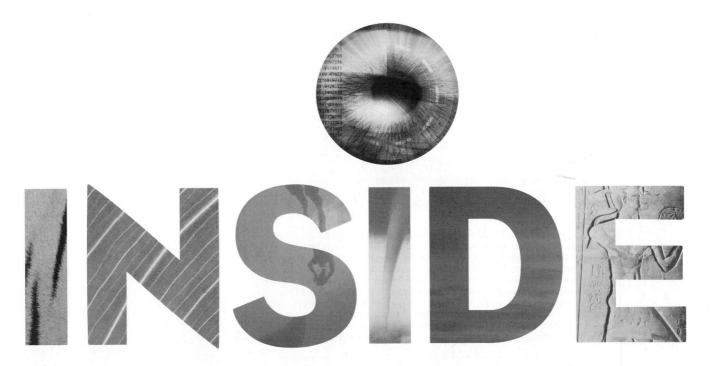

INSIDE

LANGUAGE, LITERACY, AND CONTENT

NATIONAL GEOGRAPHIC

Hampton-Brown

Acknowledgments

Grateful acknowledgment is given to our reviewers for their time and input. Grateful acknowledgment is given to the authors, artists, photographers, museums, publishers, and agents for permission to reprint copyrighted material. Every effort has been made to secure the appropriate permission. If any omissions have been made or if corrections are required, please contact the Publisher.

Photographic Credits

5 Mark Crosse/Fresno Bee/AP Images. **9** (l) Steve Schaefer/Nike/AP Images; (tr) The New York Times/Redux; (br) C Squared Studios/Photodisc/Getty Images. **15** (l) David Young-Wolff/Stone/Getty Images; (r) H. Mark Weidman Photography/ Alamy. **30** (l) David Deas/DK Stock/Getty Images; (r) UpperCut Images/Alamy. **35** (l) Werner Forman/Art Resource, NY. **39** (l) Lisa Zador/PhotoDisc/Getty Images. **45** (l) Dominic Burke/Alamy; (r) Steve Warmowski/Journal-Courier/The Image Works. **60** (l) Heide Benser/zefa/Corbis; (r) apply pictures/Alamy Images. **65** Topham/The Image Works. **66** Neil Armstrong/ Keystone/CNP/Getty Images. **67** Corbis. **82** (l) Gilles Mingasson/Getty Images; (r) Lise Aserud/Scanpix/AP Images. **83** (l) *Fishing with Spear and Lure*, 1979, Harry Egutak and Mona Ohoveluk. Stencil, Dennos Museum Center, courtesy Northwestern Michigan College, Traverse City, Michigan, permission of Holman Eskimo Co-op. **84** Frances Benjamin Johnston/Corbis. **90** (l) ColorBlind Images/Iconica/Getty Images; (r) David Young-Wolff/ Photographer's Choice/Getty Images. **95** (l) NASA, ESA, and E. Karkoschka (University of Arizona); (r) NASA/Newsmakers/ Getty Images. **105** (l) Design Pics/Alamy Images; (r) Ryan McVay/Digital Vision/Getty Images. **114** (l) Bob Rives, courtesy of Bob Rives and Vollis Simpson. **120** (l) Tim Pannell/Corbis; (r) Corbis.

Art Credits

5 (dragon) Cheryl Kirk Noll, **7** (cafeteria) Ben Shannon, **20** (water chart, glass) Dartmouth Publishing, Inc., **22** (farmers) Seitu Hayden, **24** (water decrease chart, rain barrel, Santa Fe map) Dartmouth Publishing, Inc., **35** (stork, tr) Paul Mirocha, **37** (Nile map, Egypt harvest timeline) Dartmouth Publishing, Inc., **39** (tornado map, mr) Dartmouth Publishing, Inc., **50** (sidewalk, teen and man) Ben Shannon, **54** (teens arguing, teen in class) Ben Shannon, **67** (lab objects, tr) Dartmouth Publishing, Inc., **68** (pharmacy) Ben Shannon, **69** (Hopi border, locust) Durga Bernhard, **70** (frog and locust) Durga Bernhard, **84** (women's rights chart) Dartmouth Publishing, Inc., **96** (solar system) Paul Mirocha, **97** (comet tr, comit orbit br) Paul Mirocha , **99** (gems, Olympus) Dartmouth Publishing, Inc., **110** (teen and grandmother) Dartmouth Publishing, Inc. **112** (teen and grandfather) Ben Shannon.

National Geographic School Publishing
Hampton-Brown
P.O. Box 223220
Carmel, California 93922

www.NGSP.com

Printed in the United States of America.

ISBN 978-07362-5687-2

08 09 10 11 12 13 14 15 16 17 10 9 8 7 6 5 4 3 2 1

Contents

Unit 1: Finding Your Own Place 1
Unit Test for Progress Monitoring: Reading and Language Test 2
Unit Test for Progress Monitoring: Writing Test 11

Unit 2: Water for Life 16
Unit Test for Progress Monitoring: Reading and Language Test 17
Unit Test for Progress Monitoring: Writing Test 26

Unit 3: Natural Forces. 31
Unit Test for Progress Monitoring: Reading and Language Test 32
Unit Test for Progress Monitoring: Writing Test 41

Unit 4: Creepy Classics. 46
Unit Test for Progress Monitoring: Reading and Language Test 47
Unit Test for Progress Monitoring: Writing Test 56

Unit 5: The Drive to Discover. 61
Unit Test for Progress Monitoring: Reading and Language Test 62
Unit Test for Progress Monitoring: Writing Test 71

Unit 6: Struggle for Freedom. 76
Unit Test for Progress Monitoring: Reading and Language Test 77
Unit Test for Progress Monitoring: Writing Test 86

Unit 7: Star Power 91
Unit Test for Progress Monitoring: Reading and Language Test 92
Unit Test for Progress Monitoring: Writing Test 101

Unit 8: Art and Soul 106
Unit Test for Progress Monitoring: Reading and Language Test 107
Unit Test for Progress Monitoring: Writing Test 116

Unit 1: Finding Your Own Place

Unit Test for Progress Monitoring:
   Reading and Language Test 2
Unit Test for Progress Monitoring: Writing Test 11

Reading and Language Test: Unit 1

VOCABULARY

Directions: Read each question and choose the best answer.

1 Which word means "mad at someone or something"?

   A angry

   B curious

   C familiar

   D different

2 Which word means "something new and different"?

   A adjust

   B relative

   C change

   D tradition

3 Which word means "to go away from a place"?

   A leave

   B learn

   C culture

   D understand

4 Which word means "a good chance to do something"?

   A community

   B understand

   C opportunity

   D neighborhood

5 Which word means "plain"?

   A native

   B curious

   C different

   D ordinary

6 Which word means "to have the same ideas as someone"?

   A adjust

   B agree

   C culture

   D familiar

7 Which word means "the number of people who live somewhere"?

   A adjust

   B arrange

   C immigrant

   D population

8 Which word means "a special event or party"?

   A culture

   B festival

   C relative

   D neighborhood

9 Which word means "the subject of a piece of writing or of a discussion"?

   A topic

   B value

   C tradition

   D community

10 Which word means "to make an idea clear so people can understand it"?

   A analyze

   B explain

   C arrange

   D compare

11 Which word means "to get from two or more different places"?

   A learn

   B value

   C native

   D collect

12 Which word means "the parts nearby that help explain the meaning"?

   A culture

   B strange

   C context

   D immigrant

UNIT 1

GO ON

Reading and Language Test: Unit 1, *continued*

GRAMMAR & SENTENCE STRUCTURE

Directions: For each question, read the sentences in the box. Then read the question and choose the best answer.

13
> My parents is from New York. You can tell by their accent.

The word is should be changed to

A be

B am

C are

D No change

14
> I are a basketball fan. I like to watch all the teams.

The word are should be changed to

A is

B be

C am

D No change

15
> He plays the guitar like a rock star. He am the best musician at our school.

The word am should be changed to

A is

B be

C are

D No change

16
> You are lucky to know three languages. I have to study hard to speak two languages.

The word are should be changed to

A is

B be

C am

D No change

17
> We write for the town newspaper. We is a good group of reporters.

The word is should be changed to

A be

B am

C are

D No change

GO ON

Reading and Language Test: Unit 1, *continued*

 Turn right at the traffic light, Then, look for the baseball field.

The first sentence should be changed to

A Right turn at the traffic light.

B Right turn at the traffic light?

C Turn right at the traffic light.

D No change

 I am from Russia. You are from where?

How should the second sentence be written?

A Where are you from?

B Where from are you?

C Where you are from?

D No change

 We have not met. My neighbor you are?

How should the second sentence be written?

A Are you my neighbor?

B Are you my neighbor.

C You are my neighbor

D No change

 I think we should leave soon. We don't know exactly when the movie starts.

How should the second sentence be written?

A Do we know exactly when the movie starts.

B Exactly when the movie starts we don't know?

C We don't know exactly when the movie starts?

D No change

 I have a cold. Please go to the store and buy some orange juice?

The second sentence should be changed to

A Please go to the store and buy some orange juice.

B Go to the store please and buy some orange juice

C Go to the store and please buy some orange juice!

D No change

GO ON

Reading and Language Test: Unit 1, *continued*

READING COMPREHENSION & LITERARY ANALYSIS

Directions: Questions 23–26 are about "New Year's Celebrations." Read the selection.
Then read each question and choose the best answer.

New Year's Celebrations

The United States has many cultures. This is one reason this country is great. Here, cultures from around the world meet and blend. Immigrants bring rich traditions. These traditions help people remember their homelands. They also give the United States many colorful celebrations. In some ways, the celebrations here are just like those in other countries. In other ways, the celebrations are different here.

Some of the most colorful events are New Year's celebrations. The biggest celebrations in the United States are held on December 31 and January 1. Other celebrations take place at different times.

Between January 21 and February 19, some cities in the United States celebrate the Chinese New Year, *Yuan Tan*. San Francisco has the biggest event. Some New Year's activities are similar to those practiced in China. People give children red envelopes for luck in both countries. A big dragon parade is traditional in China. In the United States, the parade might also have marching bands and floats. The parade shows a blend of cultures.

The people of Laos are known as Hmong. A number of American cities hold Hmong New Year's Festivals. Festivals usually happen here in November or December, though in some cities they may be as early as September. Some of the biggest celebrations are held in Fresno, California,

and Minneapolis, Minnesota. At the festivals, Hmong young people play a ball-toss game. Just as in Laos, this game gives young people a chance to get to know each other. It also gives them a chance to wear beautiful clothes. In both countries, families celebrate together. They sing, dance, and eat traditional foods. New Year's is a great time for young and old to be together.

Hmong young people celebrating the New Year in Fresno, California.

Many traditions both continue and blend in the United States. People enjoy celebrating them together. Celebrations from many cultures make the United States a more interesting place for everyone.

GO ON ➡

23 What is the topic of this selection?

   A how different cultures celebrate a holiday

   B how some celebrations have changed over time

   C how cities have different festivals during the year

   D how children from different cultures play different games

24 The writer organizes the ideas in this selection by

   A year.

   B culture.

   C age group.

   D time order.

25 Which meaning of the word <u>floats</u> is used in this selection?

   A rafts or parts of a dock

   B decorated cars or vehicles

   C objects that support a fishing line

   D objects that stay on top of the water

26 Which of these traditions is followed in both China and the United States?

   A Children play a ball-toss game.

   B Children receive a red envelope for luck.

   C The New Year's parade has marching bands.

   D The New Year's parade is held in the largest city.

GO ON ▶

Reading and Language Test: Unit 1, *continued*

Directions: Questions 27–31 are about "The Two Pauls." Read the selection.
Then read each question and choose the best answer.

The Two Pauls

"Why did we have to move to this new apartment?" I asked my mother for the thirteenth time. In my old neighborhood, I had friends. I knew the neighbors. There was a park just two blocks away. Then suddenly I was living in a strange apartment house surrounded by total strangers.

"There's a boy your age who lives upstairs," my mother said. "His name is Paul, too." Later that day, my mother and Paul's mother introduced us. We didn't seem to have much in common except our names. He was short, and I'm tall. He had lived there all his life, and I was new. He liked the Cubs. I'm a White Sox fan. We spent five minutes staring at our shoes. Then I said I had to go downstairs and unpack my license plate collection.

Paul laughed when I said that. I don't know why he laughed. What was wrong with collecting license plates? I wondered. They were really interesting to me.

The next day, I started at my new school. I was in Paul's class. The teacher called us Paul B and Paul L. I didn't think Paul B liked me very much. After all, in the past, he had been the only Paul.

I didn't know where to sit in the cafeteria, so I sat alone at an empty table. Paul B was eating with his friends. They were all laughing and having fun. Was he telling them that I collected license plates? Was that why they were laughing? I thought about saying something, but what was the <u>point</u>? They probably would not care.

The lunch hour seemed to take forever. Finally, the bell rang. To get to my classroom, I had to walk past the table where Paul B and his friends were sitting. I was afraid they would laugh at me.

Paul B called my name as I passed. I turned, ready for anything. He didn't laugh, though. In fact, he introduced me to his friends, Bonnie and Tyrel.

"Why did you eat all alone?" Bonnie asked me. "There are seats here at our table."

"I thought you were laughing at me," I blurted out. "I thought you were laughing at my license plate collection." My face turned red. I couldn't believe I had just said that.

"We wouldn't laugh at that!" Paul B replied. "Old license plates are cool. I collect old hubcaps myself. Come over after school and I'll show you."

GO ON

UNIT 1

As it turned out, Paul and I have a lot in common. We both have road bikes, and we like to ride them to the lake to go fishing. Science is our favorite subject, and we like the same movies.

Paul and I are both into baseball, too. As I said before, he's a Cubs fan, and I'll always root for the White Sox. It's not a problem, though. We agree to disagree. In fact, last week, his dad took us to a Cubs game, and I have to admit it was pretty good. And for my birthday next month, Mom is getting White Sox tickets. I guess I shouldn't have been surprised when Paul said he'd like to go with me. After all, that's what good friends do!

27 The author organizes the ideas in this selection by

    A explaining the most important events first.

    B explaining a problem and what caused it.

    C describing the old neighborhood and then the new neighborhood.

    D telling about events in the order they happened.

28 What is one way that Paul B and Paul L are alike?

    A They both have unusual collections.

    B They both have moved to new homes.

    C They both feel uncomfortable at school.

    D They both cheer for the same baseball team.

29 Which meaning of the word point is used in this selection?

    A the location of something

    B the sharp end of an object

    C a unit for keeping score in a game

    D a purpose or reason for doing something

30 What is one way that Paul B and Paul L are different?

    A Paul B likes history, and Paul L likes science.

    B Paul B enjoys fishing, and Paul L enjoys swimming.

    C Paul B lives in a house, and Paul L lives in an apartment.

    D Paul B knows the neighborhood, and Paul L is new there.

31 What is the topic of this selection?

    A parents

    B bicycles

    C new friends

    D license plates

GO ON ➡

UNIT 1

Reading and Language Test: Unit 1, *continued*

Directions: Questions 32–36 are about "The Power of Soccer." Read the selection.
Then read each question and choose the best answer.

The Power of Soccer

No matter where you live, you probably know something about soccer. It is the world's most popular sport. Soccer can have the power to bring people together. Luma Mufleh knows this very well. She is a soccer coach in Clarkston, Georgia. She helps young people come together <u>through</u> soccer. Soccer has helped her players feel more connected to each other. As a result, they feel more connected to their community.

Luma Mufleh, founder of the Fugees soccer team

Years ago, Mufleh learned about many young people who were new to the town of Clarkston. Thousands of families had moved to Clarkston to build a new life in the United States. Mufleh knew that it takes time to adjust to a new place. She had moved to the United States from Jordan not that long before.

Mufleh thought that many of the young people in Clarkston would enjoy soccer. Many of them enjoyed it in their home countries. Mufleh wanted to help them <u>settle</u> into their new home town. This gave her an idea to start her own soccer team in Clarkston. She created many posters in different languages about the new soccer team. She wanted as many people to join the team as possible.

Mufleh welcomed over twenty players the first day. Players came from all backgrounds. Playing soccer was something they all wanted. Many of the kids had never played for a coach. Many of the new players did not know how to be part of a team.

Members of the "Fugees" are part of a boy's soccer program for refugees in Clarkston, Georgia.

Mufleh and her team trained for many hours. The team members played in jeans and t-shirts instead of uniforms. They practiced on a dusty field with no goal posts.

After a few weeks, the players learned to trust and rely on each other on the soccer field. They did very well. Mufleh's team even had a large number of supporters. People in Clarkston saw the big difference soccer made in the lives of these young people.

Mufleh's team members also became good friends off the soccer field. One player said, "It's like they're all from my own country. They're my brothers." Through soccer, Mufleh's team found their place in the community.

GO ON

Reading and Language Test: Unit 1, continued

32 What is the main idea of this selection?

A why a coach is important to a team

B how a sport can bring people together

C how a team can practice to win games

D why people feel strange in a new place

33 What is the main idea of paragraph 4?

A There were too many people for the team.

B People from different backgrounds came to play.

C Few people came out for the team because they had never met the coach.

D Players knew the game well because they had played in their home countries.

34 What would be the best heading for paragraph 5?

A The First Day

B A Plan to Succeed

C Becoming a Team

D Winning the First Game

35 Which meaning of the word <u>through</u> is used in this selection?

A finished

B by a common interest in

C over a whole distance

D from beginning to end

36 Which meaning of the word <u>settle</u> is used in this selection?

A to agree upon

B to calm or quiet

C to make a home

D to pay what is owed

READING STRATEGY

Directions: Read question 37. Write your answer on a separate sheet of paper.

37 Rodrigo is getting ready to read "The Power of Soccer." Before he begins, he wants to plan his reading. Write to recommend a strategy that you use to plan your reading:

1. Explain the strategy.

2. Give an example of how to use it, based on specific information from the selection.

DONE!

Writing Test: Unit 1

REVISING & EDITING

Directions: Read the composition. It contains errors. Then read each question and choose the best answer.

Grandmother's Memoir

(1) When I was fifteen years old, my family moved to a new house. (2) While packing, my mother found an old suitcase in the attic. (3) Inside it was something that my grandmother had written.

(4) "When I was eight years old I left Naples, Italy, for the United States. (5) The year was 1905. (6) My father had been living across the Atlantic for three years. (7) Life was hard in Naples. (8) Father went to the United States to make a better life for us. (9) My mother read the memoir aloud.

(10) In New York, father worked in the clothing industry. (11) He used giant machines to sew shirts. (12) He usually worked ten hours a day, including weekends! (13) He made $5.00 a week. (14) Slowly, he saved the money we needed to buy our tickets.

(15) We had to stay on the lower deck of the steamship. (16) It was crowded, noisy, and it smelled bad. (17) It took eight days to cross the ocean.

(18) When we finally reached New York Harbor, we sailed past the Statue of Liberty. (19) We landed at a place called Ellis Island. (20) Once inside the giant, red brick building, we each had to have a medical exam, and my mother had to answer many questions. (21) Finally we met my father. (22) It was so wonderful to see him again!

(23) In our new neighborhood, we had many Italian neighbors. (24) The sights, sounds, and smells were all familiar. (25) Some things were different. (26) At first we had to stay home from school to help father with sewing. (27) My brother sold newspapers on the street. (28) My mother did laundry for other people.

(29) When I went to school, I worked hard to learn English. (30) Now I was having a difficult time getting good grades.

(31) Sometimes I missed Italy, but mostly I was happy to be in the United States. (32) It felt like my home."

GO ON

Writing Test: Unit 1, *continued*

1 Sentence 9 should be moved

   A after sentence 3

   B before sentence 19

   C after sentence 32

   D No change

2 Which sentence should be added before sentence 15 to begin the paragraph?

   A Many people got sick from the crowded conditions.

   B One night there was a fierce storm with giant waves.

   C But when the time came to travel, we were disappointed.

   D Those were the longest eight days that I ever lived through.

3 Which signal word should be added to the beginning of sentence 25 to show a contrast with the sentence before it?

   A But

   B Also

   C Similarly

   D In the same way

4 Which sentence should be added before sentence 30?

   A My teachers told me to work even harder.

   B In Naples I had been a straight 'A' student.

   C My brother was still selling newspapers to help my parents.

   D Although my father's English was not perfect, people understood him.

GO ON ▶

Writing Test: Unit 1, *continued*

Directions: Read the composition. It contains errors. Then read each question and choose the best answer.

Finding Home: A Place in the Alps

(1) I was born and raised in New York City, home of skyscrapers, subways, and over 8 million people. (2) I once called another country my home, though. (3) That country was Switzerland, where I lived for several years.

(4) After I finished college, I went to Europe. (5) I visited many countries. (6) When I reached Switzerland, I took a train that went straight up the side of a mountain!

(7) I soon discovered a storybook village. (8) There were cute cottages with wooden balconies. (9) There were flower boxes with colorful flowers. (10) There were two roads in the village and there were no cars! (11) Everyone walked. (12) Can you imagine this (13) There was one grocery store and one school.

(14) Many people in the village were farmers. (15) Every summer, the farmers herded their cows up to the high mountains. (16) <u>these high mountains</u> are called *alps*. (17) On the alps, there are sweet grass fields. (18) The sweet grass helps the herd produce rich milk.

(19) I lived on an alp for a summer. (20) To get to my home, I had to hike up a very steep and long trail. (21) It took over three hours! (22) On the alp, I lived in a wooden hut that was over 200 years old. (23) The hut had no electricity or water. (24) <u>We cooked all</u> our meals over a fire. (25) We got our water from a nearby spring.

(26) Life on the alp taught me important skills. (27) I learned to chop wood for the fire that kept us warm. (28) I looked after the cows and goats that gave us milk. (29) I cooked the milk to make delicious cheese. (30) I learned to build a fence to keep the animals penned in. (31) I made tea from wild <u>herbs?</u> (32) I carried heavy supplies up and down steep trails.

(33) During my time in the Swiss Alps, I learned that I can do and be anything. (34) I also found a new place to call home.

Writing Test: Unit 1, *continued*

5 In sentence 12, <u>this</u> should be changed to

   A   this,

   B   this?

   C   this.

   D   No change

6 In sentence 16, <u>these high mountains</u> should be changed to

   A   these high Mountains

   B   These High mountains

   C   These high mountains

   D   No change

7 In sentence 24, <u>We cooked all</u> should be changed to

   A   we cooked all

   B   we Cooked All

   C   We Cooked all

   D   No change

8 In sentence 31, <u>herbs?</u> should be changed to

   A   herbs,

   B   herbs.

   C   herbs

   D   No change

GO ON ➤

Name _____ Date _____

Writing Test: Unit 1, *continued*

Directions: Read writing prompts A and B. Choose one to write a composition. Write on separate sheets of paper. Use the Writer's Checklist to make sure that you do your best work.

Prompt A

Think of your favorite food. Imagine that you are sharing this food with people who have never tried it before. Write a paragraph to explain to them why this food is your favorite.

---------------- **OR** ----------------

Prompt B

Most people enjoy doing the things they are good at. Think of your favorite sport or a hobby. Write a paragraph that tells why you enjoy this sport or hobby.

Writer's Checklist

Does your composition

☑ have a topic sentence that states the main idea?

☑ contain details or examples that tell more about the main idea?

☑ present all the ideas in the best order?

DONE!

Unit 2: Water for Life

Unit Test for Progress Monitoring:
    Reading and Language Test 17
Unit Test for Progress Monitoring: Writing Test 26

Reading and Language Test: Unit 2

VOCABULARY

Directions: Read each question and choose the best answer.

1 Which word means "to move freely"?

- **A** flow
- **B** worry
- **C** depend
- **D** generate

2 Which word means "a model of a person or thing"?

- **A** crop
- **B** treat
- **C** statue
- **D** electricity

3 Which word means "just right"?

- **A** plan
- **B** alive
- **C** safely
- **D** perfect

4 Which word means "energy that makes things work"?

- **A** treat
- **B** globe
- **C** power
- **D** amount

5 Which word means "a very small town"?

- **A** crop
- **B** village
- **C** material
- **D** amount

6 Which word means "to reach a place"?

- **A** plan
- **B** arrive
- **C** depend
- **D** generate

7 Which word means "things that people buy and sell"?

- **A** goods
- **B** secret
- **C** rainfall
- **D** amount

8 Which word means "here and ready for use"?

- **A** alive
- **B** safely
- **C** secret
- **D** available

9 Which word means "exact"?

- **A** series
- **B** arrange
- **C** context
- **D** specific

10 Which word means "a group of items that are related in some way"?

- **A** analyze
- **B** tradition
- **C** category
- **D** immigrant

11 Which word means "to put something in writing"?

- **A** collect
- **B** record
- **C** support
- **D** compare

12 Which word means "to think about how two things are connected"?

- **A** learn
- **B** relate
- **C** explain
- **D** support

GO ON

UNIT 2

Reading and Language Test: Unit 2, continued

GRAMMAR & SENTENCE STRUCTURE

Directions: For each question, read the sentences in the box. Then read the question and choose the best answer.

 13

> We all love the end of the school year. The partys are always fun.

The word partys should be changed to

A party

B parties

C partyes

D No change

14

> The lights went out during the storm. We lit several lantern.

The word lantern should be changed to

A lanterns

B lanternes

C lanternies

D No change

 15

> Animals often behave in special ways. Foxs are known for being smart and shy.

The word Foxs should be changed to

A Fox

B Foxes

C Foxies

D No change

 16

> France is a country with an interesting history. The old churches there are very beautiful.

The word churches should be changed to

A church

B churchs

C churchies

D No change

 17

> I love cats and dogs. This year, I am a helper at the animal shelter.

The word am should be changed to

A is

B be

C are

D No change

 18

> He practiced all summer. Now, he are the best soccer player on the team.

The word are should be changed to

A is

B am

C be

D No change

UNIT 2

GO ON

Reading and Language Test: Unit 2, *continued*

19 | California is an interesting state. The mountains <u>has</u> many lakes and campgrounds. |

The word <u>has</u> should be changed to

A have

B to have

C having

D No change

20 | You <u>have</u> so many different skills. You will be very <u>helpful</u> to us. |

The word <u>have</u> should be changed to

A has

B to have

C having

D No change

21 | They plan to travel to all the continents. They <u>be</u> real adventurers. |

The word <u>be</u> should be changed to

A is

B am

C are

D No change

22 | History can be confusing. The teacher <u>do</u> a good job of explaining events. |

The word <u>do</u> should be changed to

A does

B to do

C doing

D No change

GO ON

UNIT 2

Reading and Language Test: Unit 2, *continued*

READING COMPREHENSION & LITERARY ANALYSIS

Directions: Questions 23–26 are about "Water's Worth." Read the selection.
Then read each question and choose the best answer.

Water's Worth

"When the well is dry, we know the worth of water."   —*Benjamin Franklin*, 1746

What did Ben Franklin mean? When something is gone, we understand how much we need it. This is especially true for water. Every living thing on Earth needs water. Without water, there is no life.

It may seem that we will never run out of water. However, let's look at the facts. Ninety-seven percent of Earth's water is in our oceans. It is too salty for drinking. Another two percent is trapped in ice, glaciers, or snow. This leaves only one percent. This is used by plants, animals, and humans.

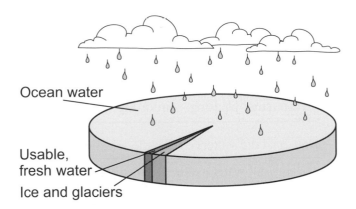

Ocean water

Usable, fresh water

Ice and glaciers

Pie Chart of Earth's Water

Earth's usable water supply is <u>precious</u>. Many communities around the world don't have enough. They need clean water for drinking, cooking, and washing. Their rivers and lakes are polluted. Many water supplies are decreasing. This problem could grow if we keep polluting or overusing our water supplies. Experts worry that the small percentage of usable water will not last. Governments and individuals are trying to solve this problem. We can help, too.

Losing our water can be <u>frightening</u> to think about. But it is not too late to change it. Today there are a lot of products to help us save water. We can find low-flow shower heads. We can buy rainwater collecting systems. There are even systems which save water that falls onto the pavement. Usually, water runs off hard pavement and into drains. From there it flows, untreated, into bodies of water. But there is a way to fix this. Instead of using hard cement for sidewalks, builders can use special kinds of sand, dirt, or other materials. When water hits these materials, it flows through and into the ground. There it is cleaned as part of the natural water cycle. Products like these can be used widely.

We can also do simple things to help make sure our clean water supply lasts. Here are just a few.

- Take five-minute showers.

- Turn off the water when brushing your teeth.

- Pick one glass to use all day for drinking water.

- Do not pre-rinse dishes in the sink before washing.

- Ask for water at a restaurant only if you will drink it.

- Ask your parents to get a shower head and toilet that use less water.

GO ON

UNIT 2

Reading and Language Test: Unit 2, continued

- Choose plants for your yard that need little watering.

- Reuse water collected in rain barrels for your indoor and outdoor plants.

Today, more governments are thinking about ways to save water. More importantly, people are doing things to save water. We are learning the worth of water.

23 What is the main idea of the selection?

A Earth has a good supply of water.

B Earth has ways to clean its water.

C People should grow plants that need little water.

D People can do easy things to save needed water.

24 Which word means the opposite of precious?

A pretty

B special

C active

D worthless

25 Which detail explains why Earth has a small amount of drinking water?

A It may seem that we will never run out of water.

B Ninety-seven percent of Earth's water is in our oceans.

C Experts worry that the small percentage of usable water will not last.

D Governments and individuals are trying to solve this problem.

26 Read the thesaurus entry below.

> **Main Entry:** frightening
> **Part of Speech:** adjective
> **Definition:** shocking
> **Synonyms:** alarming, awful, dreadful, horrid, scary, spooky, threatening
> **Antonyms:** pleasing, comforting

Now read the sentence from the selection.

> Losing our water can be frightening to think about.

In this sentence, the word frightening means the same as

A alarming.

B spooky.

C pleasing.

D comforting.

UNIT 2

GO ON →

Reading and Language Test: Unit 2, *continued*

Directions: Questions 27–32 are about "A Farmer's Helpers." Read the selection. Then read each question and choose the best answer.

A Farmer's Helpers

John walked through the late winter snow into town. He heard a noise outside his neighbor David's farmhouse. Walking up the lane, he saw his neighbor tossing seeds on the ground for the birds. They flocked toward him in great numbers.

"You're a fool two ways, David Johnson," said John as he shook his head.

"Why do you say that?" David replied as he continued feeding the birds.

"First, you are wasting the seeds you will need in the spring. Second, you are teaching these birds to come to your farm when they're hungry. I suppose, come springtime, you'll be putting nests in your fields so they won't have to travel far to get food for their babies."

David laughed softly.

"I'm happy to make room for these birds on my land," David replied. "In fact, I couldn't work without them."

The following July, John was again on the footpath between his farm and David's. Suddenly, he heard a <u>sound</u> similar to the one he remembered from the winter before. Looking over the gate, John watched as David finished pouring seeds onto the ground for a giant flock of screeching birds.

"I told you this would happen," John said smugly as the birds finished their breakfast and took to the air.

"Yes, you did," replied David pleasantly. His gaze turned from his neighbor to his own field. Tall, sturdy wheat stalks swayed in the morning breeze.

John turned, too, and was shocked by what he saw. "I don't believe it," he stammered. "I've done so much to keep the birds away from my fields. Your wheat is still five times taller than mine. How can this be?"

"Come back at dusk. Then you will see," David replied simply, as he walked toward his fields.

That evening, John arrived at David's doorstep and waited for him. As David walked to the door, he glanced over John's head and pointed his finger at a small black dot in the sky moving toward

them from the east. What appeared to be a large dark rain cloud was approaching at great speed. A moment later, the cloud had arrived at David's farm. To John's amazement, it seemed to hover in place above them. Before long, a light rain began to fall. Gently, the water dropped from the sky until all of David's crops were soaked. John noticed that none of the rain seemed to be falling on his crops. It was as though it refused to fall on his fields.

A loud shriek startled John from his thoughts. He looked up to see what had made the noise. To his surprise, what he had thought to be a rain cloud was, in fact, a great flock of birds. It was now breaking apart as the birds went to their nests in the trees.

"They fly to the lake after breakfast," David said, ending his silence. "When they return, they all carry with them a small amount of water on their backs for my fields. I give to them, and

GO ON ➡

UNIT 2

they give to me. Everyone pays a small price to guarantee the success of us all."

"That is remarkable," John replied in awe. "How did you ever learn this?"

David thought for a moment and then chuckled. "It was something my father told me. He said that farming is the easiest job in the world, as long as you know how to make it rain."

---

27 Which of these happens first in the story?

A John tells David he is a fool.

B David feeds the birds in the winter.

C John sees a large flock of birds.

D David shows John the dark cloud in the sky.

28 What is true about John at the beginning of the story?

A He thinks that David is a better farmer than he is.

B He realizes that he and David should work together.

C He does not understand why David is feeding the birds.

D He is unhappy that the crops have not been doing well.

29 What is the black dot in the sky?

A a rain storm

B a small plane

C a flock of birds

D a swarm of insects

30 What is the main problem that the farmers face?

A how to get more land for their fields

B how to get enough water for their crops

C how to keep the birds from eating their crops

D how to spread the seeds throughout their fields

31 How are friendships important in this selection?

A The farmers all work together.

B David helps John, and John helps David.

C The birds help David, and David helps the birds.

D David and his father are good neighbors to the other farmers.

32 Read these sentences from the selection.

> Suddenly, he heard a sound similar to the one he remembered from the winter before. Looking over the gate, John watched as David finished pouring seeds onto the ground for a giant flock of screeching birds.

Which is the best synonym for the word sound in the first sentence?

A thud

B echo

C racket

D crash

GO ON

UNIT 2

Reading and Language Test: Unit 2, *continued*

Directions: Questions 33–36 are about "A Question of Water." Read the selection. Then read each question and choose the best answer.

A Question of Water

Where does your household water come from? If you are not sure of the answer, you are not alone. Many people do not know where their water comes from. If you live in a dry climate, knowing the answer to this question is even more important. Santa Fe, New Mexico, is finding new answers to the question: "Where will our water come from?"

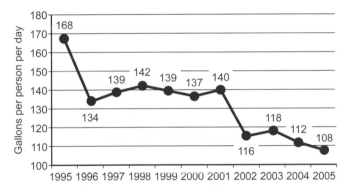

Decreasing water in use in Santa Fe from 1995 to 2005.

Santa Fe has a dry climate. It once had a flowing river called the Santa Fe River. This river provided enough water for the entire community. Healthy plants and trees grew along the banks of the Santa Fe River. Fish and other animals lived in the river. The water was clean and pure. The people of Santa Fe made great use of the river. They drank from it. They used it to water their gardens. They used it to provide water to their houses. They also used it to wash with. Over the years, the population of Santa Fe grew larger. More and more people used the river. The river grew smaller and smaller. The way the river was being used could not continue.

Santa Fe had to find a new water source. One place the city looked was underground. Rain and melting snow soak down through the soil. Water collects in pockets underground. This type of water

is called groundwater. People in the city dug wells to pump this water up to the surface. Today, most of Santa Fe's water comes from these wells.

The city of Santa Fe also began teaching people about water use. One lesson was how to be more responsible about water. Many households were using over half of their water outside. That meant that a good place to start saving water was out in the yard. People began to plant native plants, those that grow naturally in an area, instead of lawns. Native plants of Santa Fe need less water to stay green.

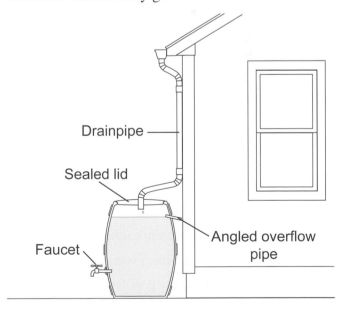

A rain barrel collects and saves water for gardening.

GO ON ➡

Reading and Language Test: Unit 2, *continued*

People also began watering their plants with rainwater. They did this by placing large barrels beside their houses. When it rains, the water pours off the roof and down drainpipes. These pipes lead to the barrels and fill them up. A hose comes from the bottom of the barrel. When it is time to water plants, all you have to do is turn the faucet at the bottom of the barrel. Gravity forces the water out of the barrel, through the hose.

Over the years, people in Santa Fe have thought a lot about where their water comes from. They have also learned smart ways to use their water. As a result, they have reduced how much water they use. In fact, Santa Fe now uses water more responsibly than most other cities in the United States!

33 Which of these **best** describes Santa Fe?

A a model for smart water use

B a city that wastes its clean water

C a place with many natural sources of water

D a town where farmers need water to make a living

34 Read these words from the selection.

river, snow, rain

Which of these words fit into the same word category?

A native

B gravity

C drainpipes

D groundwater

35 What happened to the Santa Fe River?

A It was shifted to flow into city wells.

B It became polluted from careless people.

C It dried up because there was very little rain.

D It grew smaller as the population grew larger.

36 Many people in Santa Fe now water their plants with water from

A rain.

B wells.

C the river.

D indoor faucets.

READING STRATEGY

Directions: Read question 37. Write your answer on a separate sheet of paper.

37 While Sergio is reading "A Question of Water," he comes to a confusing part. Write to recommend a strategy he can use to better understand the words and ideas:

1. Explain the strategy.

2. Give an example of how to use it, based on specific information from the selection.

DONE!

Writing Test: Unit 2

Directions: Read the composition. It contains errors. Then read each question and choose the best answer.

Water for Transportation

(1) Many of the things that we use come to us on ships. (2) Food, fuel, and many other things that we buy travel on ships. (3) The lives of many people depend on these things that come to them on oceans and rivers.

(4) Some ships had to go a long way on the ocean because they had to go around continents. (5) Some boats were not able to go as far because a river ended. (6) People began to realize that connecting waterways by building canals would improve travel. (7) Canals connect bodies of water. (8) By using canals, boats could arrive faster and easier than it would take otherwise.

(9) Canals can be built to connect oceans or rivers. (10) One canal that links oceans is the Panama Canal. (11) It was built to link the Atlantic and Pacific Oceans. (12) But it was worth it, because ships no longer had to go around South America.

(13) Rivers can be shallow or have rough rapids. (14) These sections of river are hard for boats to travel over. (15) Some rivers do not connect to other waterways. (16) Before canals, people often had to carry small boats from one part of the river to another.

(17) Canals can be dug through land that is not flat. (18) When this happens, ships have to be raised or lowered through the canal. (19) The boat goes through by entering special chambers, called locks. (20) The locks have gates on both sides. (21) These gates let water in and out, so the ship can be raised or lowered.

(22) Many river canals are no longer used except for recreation. (23) Most cargo is shipped today in other ways, such as by roads, rails, and air. (24) However, the world's transportation and many of its people still depend on waterways. (25) Traveling on water is not always easy.

GO ON

Writing Test: Unit 2, *continued*

1 Which signal word should be added to the beginning of sentence 6 to help the composition flow logically?

A While

B Before

C During

D Eventually

2 Which sentence should be added before sentence 12?

A Both large and small ships used the canal.

B Today, ships pay a toll to travel the canal.

C Building the canal was quite a difficult task.

D Soon, the canal will be made even wider.

3 Which sentence should be added before sentence 13 to begin the paragraph?

A People often sail ships just for fun!

B Canals can also solve problems on rivers.

C The *Titanic* is a famous ship that was built in 1912.

D The Missouri River is the longest river in the United States.

4 Sentence 25 should be moved

A before sentence 4

B after sentence 17

C before sentence 21

D No change

UNIT 2

GO ON

Writing Test: Unit 2, *continued*

Directions: Read the composition. It contains errors. Then read each question and choose the best answer.

Desert Plants

(1) Plants are <u>master</u> at staying alive. (2) They need water just like people and animals. (3) Unlike people and animals, however, plants cannot move. (4) Still, they live in many <u>places</u>. (5) Even in the desert, plants find a way to grow. (6) But desert plants must have special ways to get water.

(7) <u>california has many</u> desert plants. (8) Joshua trees live in <u>the mojave Desert</u>. (9) <u>These trees lives</u> for a long time, too. (10) Some Joshua trees are 200 years old!

(11) To stay alive that long in the desert, the Joshua tree has two sets of roots. (12) One <u>set of roots</u> grows deep into the ground. (13) Big bulbs form on these deep roots. (14) <u>These bulbs stores</u> water for dry times. (15) The second set of roots is close to the top, or surface. (16) These roots catch any rain that falls.

(17) The prickly pear cactus has ways to stay alive, too. (18) It is like a water bottle. (19) When rain falls, the cactus fills up with water. (20) During a rain, the plant can collect enough water to last through a long dry period.

(21) The prickly pear uses water carefully. (22) Instead of leaves, it has thin, sharp spines. (23) Not much <u>water get</u> out of them. (24) The stems of the prickly pear are also coated with a wax. (25) That keeps water in, too.

(26) Finally, let's look at the creosote bush. (27) It has several tricks. (28) <u>These bushs</u> have a taproot that can go 15 feet into the soil in search of water. (29) The leaves are wax-coated, like the prickly pear's, to seal in water. (30) When it is very dry, they can even drop their leaves. (31) This reduces how much water they need. (32) Some of these plants can live for up to two years without rain.

(33) <u>These Desert plants</u> are amazing. (34) They have developed <u>waies</u> to live where it is very hot. (35) These are all examples of how <u>a plant make</u> a little water go a long way.

GO ON

UNIT 2

5 In sentence 1, <u>master</u> should be changed to

A   masters

B   masteres

C   masteries

D   No change

6 In sentence 4, <u>places</u> should be changed to

A   place

B   placees

C   placies

D   No change

7 In sentence 7, <u>california has many</u> should be changed to

A   california Has many

B   California has many

C   California has Many

D   No change

8 In sentence 8, <u>the mojave Desert</u> should be changed to

A   the Mojave Desert

B   The Mojave desert

C   The mojave desert

D   No change

9 In sentence 9, <u>These trees lives</u> should be changed to

A   These tree live

B   These tree lives

C   These trees live

D   No change

10 In sentence 12, <u>set of roots</u> should be changed to

A   Set of roots

B   set of Roots

C   Set of Roots

D   No change

11 In sentence 14, <u>These bulbs stores</u> should be changed to

A   These bulb store

B   These bulbs store

C   These bulb stores

D   No change

12 In sentence 23, <u>water get</u> should be changed to

A   waters get

B   waters gets

C   water gets

D   No change

13 In sentence 28, <u>These bushs</u> should be changed to

A   These bush

B   These bushes

C   These bushies

D   No change

14 In sentence 33, <u>These Desert plants</u> should be changed to

A   these Desert Plants

B   These desert Plants

C   These desert plants

D   No change

15 In sentence 34, <u>waies</u> should be changed to

A   way

B   ways

C   wayes

D   No change

16 In sentence 35, <u>a plant make</u> should be changed to

A   a plant makes

B   a plants make

C   a plants makes

D   No change

Writing Test: Unit 2, *continued*

WRITTEN COMPOSITION

Directions: Read writing prompts A and B. Choose one to write a composition. Write on separate sheets of paper. Use the Writer's Checklist to make sure that you do your best work.

Prompt A

Sometimes people don't agree. They must find a way to get along. Imagine that your friend wants to go to a lake, but you want to watch a movie. Together you might decide to watch a movie about a lake. Write a narrative paragraph about a time when you made an agreement with someone. Be sure to tell about the events in the order they happened.

——————————— **OR** ———————————

Prompt B

Think of a time when you made a new friend. Where were you? What were you doing? Write a narrative paragraph about the day that your friendship began. Be sure to tell about the events in the order they happened.

Writer's Checklist

Does your composition

☑ have a topic sentence that states the main idea?

☑ include details that tell about the main idea?

☑ present events in time order?

DONE!

UNIT 2

Unit 3: Natural Forces

Reading and Language Test: Unit 3

VOCABULARY

Directions: Read each question and choose the best answer.

1 Which word means "to push"?

A force

B active

C create

D collapse

2 Which word means "not safe"?

A filled

B confused

C untouched

D dangerous

3 Which word means "a sign that something bad may happen"?

A layer

B future

C volcano

D warning

4 Which word means "a place where people can safely stay"?

A shelter

B necessity

C equipment

D earthquake

5 Which word means "the outside part of something"?

A levee

B future

C surface

D necessity

6 Which word means "to leave or to get out"?

A prepare

B evacuate

C collapse

D carefully

7 Which word means "lucky"?

A active

B severe

C fortunate

D frightened

8 Which word means "an ocean storm with strong winds"?

A layer

B levee

C volcano

D hurricane

9 Which word means "to tell what something means"?

A define

B create

C series

D category

10 Which word means "to talk about something"?

A collect

B similar

C discuss

D specific

11 Which word means "a basic part of a whole"?

A topic

B element

C resource

D explanation

12 Which word means "to find something"?

A report

B locate

C support

D narrative

GO ON

Reading and Language Test: Unit 3, *continued*

GRAMMAR & SENTENCE STRUCTURE

Directions: For each question, read the sentences in the box. Then read the question and choose the best answer.

13

| Martin Luther King, Jr., was a great speaker. She spoke with true feeling and honesty. |

The word She should be changed to

A It

B He

C They

D No change

14

| The rain sounded like rocks on the roof. It made me feel glad I was safe inside. |

The word It should be changed to

A He

B She

C They

D No change

15

| The musicians played perfectly together. She made us want to dance. |

The word She should be changed to

A He

B You

C They

D No change

16

| My grandmother speaks four languages. He can teach me many things. |

The word He should be changed to

A We

B You

C She

D No change

17

| The pioneers had a difficult life. Still, they stayed brave and strong. |

The word they should be changed to

A I

B it

C he

D No change

18

| The picnic is planned for Saturday. He will be fun. |

The word He should be changed to

A It

B She

C They

D No change

GO ON ➡

Reading and Language Test: Unit 3, *continued*

19 | My cousin went to cooking class. He <u>do</u> make several different meals now.

The word <u>do</u> should be changed to

A   is

B   has

C   can

D   No change

20 | We invented a new video game. We <u>can</u> want to show it to everyone next week.

The word <u>can</u> should be changed to

A   be

B   might

C   have

D   No change

21 | I do not want any cake. You <u>would</u> have it all.

The word <u>would</u> should be changed to

A   can

B   are

C   be

D   No change

22 | The singers are well-trained. They <u>could</u> win the state contest.

The word <u>could</u> should be changed to

A   been

B   has

C   are

D   No change

GO ON

Directions: Questions 23–28 are about "Shallow Water." Read the selection. Then read each question and choose the best answer.

Shallow Water

Bakari looked out over the fields and frowned. Something wasn't right, but he couldn't say what. A flock of white storks flew in low across the rising sun. One by one, they landed in the center of his family's flooded field.

In ancient Egypt, during the time of the Pharaohs, the Nile River flooded every year. This time of year was known as *Akhet*. Several months later, the water level would drop again. This left the land ready for planting.

While the land was flooded, there was little for the farmers in Bakari's village to do. As a result, most of them traveled north. There, they could help to build Pharaoh Khufu's pyramid. Bakari wanted to go with them. But his father, Akil, said no.

This painting shows an ancient Egyptian harvest.

"Next year you will be old enough," Akil said, smiling at his son. "Keep an eye on things here until I return."

Months passed. Every morning at sunrise, Bakari walked to his family's fields. One morning the storks were wading through the fields. They were looking for their breakfast. Bakari knew that something was wrong. He stared for a long time at the birds. Then suddenly he understood.

As fast as he could, Bakari ran to his home. He told his mother what he had seen. At first she didn't understand. Then it became clear to her, too. They both agreed that Bakari must find his father quickly. Then he must bring him back to the village. He set out at once. The journey was long. Bakari was very tired when he arrived.

"If what you say is true," Akil said, after his son described what he had seen, "then the water level is going down much faster than in the past. We must all return to our fields at once to prepare for planting."

Word quickly spread among the farmers at the work site. It was soon agreed that they all must leave to tend to their fields. Akil smiled with pride as he thought of what his son had done. Bakari realized that if the fields were not planted shortly after the water went down, the crops would be poor that season. While the land closer to the river could still be planted, it would certainly not provide enough grain for the entire kingdom for the year. Bakari's wisdom and watching had saved his village.

"And all because of a flock of storks," Akil said, laughing.

"Their legs are long," replied Bakari. "But they still only stand in shallow water."

GO ON

UNIT 3

Reading and Language Test: Unit 3, *continued*

23 What is the main setting of this story?

    A   a village on the Nile

    B   a city during Akhet

    C   the temple of a Pharaoh

    D   the northern part of Egypt

24 Why is the time of year important to the story?

    A   The main character changes over time.

    B   The villagers leave every year to fight the floods.

    C   The people plan their lives around the yearly floods.

    D   The main character must make a long journey.

25 What does the word <u>shortly</u> mean in the selection?

    A   soon

    B   with no hurry

    C   after some time

    D   with great need

26 Which words **best** describe the boy in the story?

    A   proud and smart

    B   friendly and funny

    C   honest and hopeful

    D   thoughtful and wise

27 Why does the boy's father tell the boy to stay at home?

    A   He needs to take care of his mother.

    B   He is too weak to travel to the north.

    C   He is too young to help build the pyramid.

    D   He has too much work to do for his family.

28 How does the boy save his village?

    A   He warns his father that a flood is coming.

    B   He realizes that the crops should be planted soon.

    C   He keeps the storks from eating all the crop seeds.

    D   He tells his mother that there is too little food for everyone.

UNIT 3

GO ON

Reading and Language Test: Unit 3, *continued*

Directions: Questions 29–32 are about "The Nile Floods." Read the selection.
Then read each question and choose the best answer.

The Nile Floods

The muddy water rose steadily. It climbed the riverbank and spread over the fields. Soon, the Nile River stretched wide. All of Egypt's fields lay drowned beneath its waters. This scene sounds like a disaster. How could farmers grow food when their fields were flooded? What

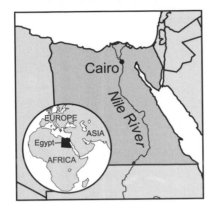

happened to people's homes when the river flooded? Floods are often terrible. However, natural disasters can sometimes lead to creative solutions. They sometimes even have positive outcomes.

In ancient times, the Nile River flooded every year. The people who lived in Egypt learned how to live with the floods. In fact, the Nile floods helped make the country stronger.

Planning for the Floods

The ancient Nile River floods started in the south of Egypt in June. By October, the floods had reached the north. Here the floodwaters were at their highest point. Egyptians learned to predict the floods. They made calendars and studied the stars. The stars changed with the seasons. One important star was called Sirius. It rose into the sky around the time the floods would begin. The position of Sirius was a sign for the Egyptians to prepare for the floods.

When the Nile began to flood, the Egyptians were ready. They built their villages at the edge of

the floodplain. They tried to build on high ground. This means that the floodwaters rarely reached the houses. The Egyptians used the land close to the river for farming. The farms were not hurt by the floodwaters.

Floods Help Farms

In fact, the Nile floods helped Egypt's farms in two ways. First, the floods brought water to the fields. Most of Egypt is very hot. It rarely rains. The floodwater covered the farms and sank into the fields. Afterward, the fields stayed wet. This helped the crops grow, even without rain.

Second, the floods improved the soil in the fields. The floodwaters washed over the land for a few weeks. Then they receded, or shrank back. The waters left behind a thick layer of rich mud. The mud was good for growing crops. It helped Egyptian farmers grow more food.

Two Ways of Living with the Nile

The Nile River does not flood anymore. In modern times, people built dams that control the river. The ancient Egyptians could not keep the Nile from flooding, but they were not powerless. They learned to live *with* the mighty river. They knew when the Nile would flood and where the floods might reach. The Nile floods were an important part of life in ancient Egypt.

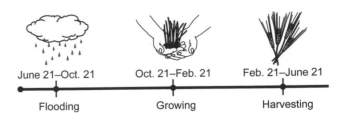

June 21–Oct. 21	Oct. 21–Feb. 21	Feb. 21–June 21
Flooding	Growing	Harvesting

GO ON ➤

UNIT 3

Reading and Language Test: Unit 3, *continued*

29 "The Nile Floods" and "Shallow Water" explain how ancient Egyptians lived with floods. How do the two selections do this?

   A "The Nile Floods" shows it in a diagram. "Shallow Water" uses pictures.

   B "The Nile Floods" uses facts. "Shallow Water" describes what characters do.

   C "The Nile Floods" has headings that tell about it. "Shallow Water" shows it in what the characters say.

   D "The Nile Floods" describes it through a person's experiences. "Shallow Water" describes what ancient Egypt was like.

30 How is "The Nile Floods" different from "Shallow Water"?

   A "Shallow Water" states a main idea, and "The Nile Floods" does not.

   B "The Nile Floods" has a plot and pictures, and "Shallow Water" does not.

   C "Shallow Water" has a setting and characters, and "The Nile Floods" does not.

   D "The Nile Floods" tells an entertaining story, and "Shallow Water" does not.

31 What does the word <u>floodplain</u> mean?

   A the direction a flood moves in

   B the part of a river that can be seen

   C the damage caused by a flooded river

   D the low land that is flooded by a river

32 What does the word <u>powerless</u> mean?

   A without power

   B an act of power

   C a state of power

   D the results of power

GO ON

Directions: Questions 33–36 are about "Tornadoes: The Twister Storms."
Read the selection. Then read each question and choose the best answer.

Tornadoes: The Twister Storms

Dorothy picked up her dog, Toto. The sky was black. The clouds were moving fast. There was a strange green color in the air. She knew there was a tornado, or twister, coming. She tried to get to the underground storm cellar. She did not have time, so she ran into the house for shelter. The wind picked up the house. The house swirled inside the tornado. Then the house hit the ground with a crash.

This scene is from the well-known story *The Wonderful Wizard of Oz* by Frank L. Baum. However, every year thousands of tornadoes occur in real life (though they may not all be as wild as the one in *The Wonderful Wizard of Oz*). Tornadoes are a natural force that thousands of people need to plan for, deal with, and recover from every year.

What is a tornado?

A tornado is a spinning column of air. This column reaches from the clouds to the ground. Tornadoes are produced by severe thunderstorms. One thunderstorm can produce many tornadoes.

A tornado spins in a tube shape. The tube acts like a vacuum cleaner. It sucks things up inside. It can pull trees out by their roots. It can destroy buildings. It can damage roads. It can move cars around as if they were toys. It can also have curious results.

Once, a tornado sucked up frogs from a pond and rained them down in another town.

The wind from a tornado turns at high speeds. These high-speed winds can <u>quickly</u> destroy entire buildings and communities. Tornadoes are usually four or five hundred feet wide. They last only a few minutes. However, monster tornadoes can be a mile wide. They can last for more than an hour. Their winds are the strongest measured in nature—sometimes up to 300 miles per hour.

Where do tornadoes happen?

Tornadoes can happen almost anywhere. They have been reported on all continents except Antarctica. They usually occur where cold air meets warm tropical air.

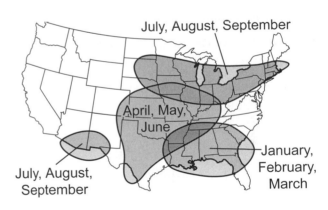

July, August, September

April, May, June

July, August, September

January, February, March

Times and Areas That Tornadoes Can Occur

Between 600 and 1000 tornadoes touch down in the United States each year. Compared to all other countries, the United States has the most tornadoes per year. It also has the most violent tornadoes in the world. Tornadoes can occur anywhere in the United States, but they are most frequent in the eastern two-thirds of the country. This is due to the frequent clash of cool, dry air meeting warm, moist maritime air that occurs over this part of the United States.

UNIT 3

Reading and Language Test: Unit 3, *continued*

How can we prepare for tornadoes?

Today, scientists keep a close watch on storms. They are often able to predict whether or not a tornado could form. They are then able to give a warning that might help save people's lives.

People who live in a tornado area should be careful when there is a storm. They should know that severe thunderstorms and a wall of clouds are signs that a tornado could form. They should listen to television or radio if these signs are present. They should try to learn if there is tornado danger.

People who live in a tornado area should also know what to do if there is a tornado warning.

For the best protection, they should go to the basement of a sturdy building. If there is no basement, they should go to an inside room or closet. They should stay away from windows. They can also get into a bathtub. Bathtubs are usually heavy and hard to move. If people are outside in open space, they should get as close to the ground as possible.

Only a small number of tornadoes strike places where there are people. Of course, it is smart to be prepared. It is smart to be aware of the signs of a tornado, and to know what to do if a tornado comes.

---

33 How is "Tornadoes: The Twister Storms" different from "The Nile Floods"?

  A It includes pictures and opinions.

  B It includes both fiction and nonfiction parts.

  C It gives information through facts and diagrams.

  D It teaches a lesson through characters and storytelling.

34 How are the diagrams in "The Nile Floods" and "Tornadoes: The Twister Storms" alike?

  A They both tell steps in a process.

  B They both show how to do something.

  C They both show the effects of natural disasters.

  D They both tell when certain natural events happen.

35 What does the word <u>quickly</u> mean?

  A in a quick way

  B without being quick

  C the result of quick action

  D the quality of being quick

36 Which of these selections is historical fiction?

  A "Shallow Water"

  B "The Nile Floods"

  C "Tornadoes: The Twister Storms"

  D "The Nile Floods" and "Tornadoes: The Twister Storms"

READING STRATEGY

Directions: Read question 37. Write your answer on a separate sheet of paper.

37 Kelvin is reading "Tornadoes: The Twister Storms." As he reads, he wants to make connections. Write to recommend a strategy that you use for making connections during reading:

  1. Explain the strategy.

  2. Give an example of how to use it, based on specific information from the selection.

DONE!

Writing Test: Unit 3

REVISING & EDITING

Directions: Read the composition. It contains errors. Then read each question and choose the best answer.

No Rain in Sight

(1) The sky had not rained for one hundred days. (2) Everything looked thirsty. (3) The lakes were dry. (4) The crops were dying. (5) Our state was going through a drought.

(6) The government leaders asked us to use less water. (7) We took shorter showers. (8) The grass was brown. (9) We turned the water off while we brushed our teeth. (10) We learned to treat water like a precious treasure.

(11) Then the good news came. (12) Our school officials said that if it did not rain by Friday, classes would not be held the following week—test week! (13) My friends and I cheered and stopped studying.

(14) Scientists and water experts were called. (15) They tried many things, but there was still no rain. (16) Then I remembered an old belief my grandfather had told me about. (17) He said some people believe that rain comes after people talk about horses. (18) On Thursday, my friends and I spent our lunchtime laughing and saying everything we could think of about horses.

(19) On Friday afternoon, the clouds grew dark. (20) It happened. (21) The rain started slowly, and then fell more quickly until it was pouring onto the dry earth. (22) Had our horse talk worked?

(23) People ran from their houses, shouting, laughing, and hugging each other. (24) It tasted like life. (25) Suddenly, all the students in the crowd stopped. (26) School would be open Monday, and we would have to take the tests! (27) As I hurried home to my books, I felt happy and worried at the same time.

GO ON ➡

Writing Test: Unit 3, *continued*

1 Sentence 8 should be moved

   A before sentence 4

   B before sentence 12

   C after sentence 22

   D No change

2 Which sentence should be added before sentence 14 to begin the paragraph?

   A People tried to make it rain.

   B People gathered to celebrate.

   C We felt drops falling from the sky.

   D We watched clouds start to gather.

3 Which transition word should be added to the beginning of sentence 20 to show a connection to the sentence before it?

   A Also

   B Then

   C Second

   D However

4 Which sentence should be added before sentence 24?

   A Streams began to swell.

   B Animals waited for water.

   C Teachers prepared for school.

   D Rain streamed down their faces.

UNIT 3

GO ON

Directions: Read the composition. It contains errors. Then read each question and choose the best answer.

December 14 2008

Dear Kelly.

(1) I thought it would be fun to visit my cousins during winter vacation. (2) My trip has already turned into quite an adventure.

(3) A few nights ago, my aunt started wrapping the pipes in the basement with blankets. (4) <u>You</u> left faucets dripping because moving water does not freeze. (5) My uncle insisted on giving me a <u>beautyful</u> quilt, although I had a good electric blanket. (6) A bad storm was coming, and we did not want to do anything <u>carless</u>. (7) <u>We</u> might be dangerous, so we needed to be prepared.

(8) During the night, the snow fell fast and thick. (9) Tree limbs fell on the power lines. (10) We had no electricity for lights, or TV, or even CDs!

(11) That day and the next were filled with work and play for me and my cousins' family. (12) <u>It</u> chopped wood, shoveled snow, and cleared branches from the yard. (13) We had snowball fights, went sledding, and drank hot chocolate by the fire. (14) My cousins Jake and Sara and I sat near the fire while Uncle Bert and Aunt Claire told <u>funi</u> stories. (15) <u>I</u> was exhausted, but I had a great time.

(16) <u>Finalily</u> the electric company finished repairing the electric lines. (17) Trucks with plows cleared the roads. (18) They worked all day because the snow was so deep.

(19) Snow can be dangerous and threatening, but I got to see another side of it. (20) I got to see the fun side that brings a family together.

(21) I hope you are doing well. (22) Write to me soon.

Your friend,

Jessica

GO ON ➡

5 December 14 2008 should be changed to

A   december 14 2008

B   december 14, 2008

C   December 14, 2008

D   No change

6 Dear Kelly. should be changed to

A   Dear Kelly

B   Dear Kelly,

C   Dear kelly

D   No change

7 In sentence 4, You should be changed to

A   It

B   He

C   She

D   No change

8 In sentence 5, beautyful should be changed to

A   beautiful

B   beauttful

C   beauteful

D   No change

9 In sentence 6, carless should be changed to

A   cariless

B   carrless

C   careless

D   No change

10 In sentence 7, We should be changed to

A   I

B   It

C   He

D   No change

11 In sentence 12, It should be changed to

A   We

B   He

C   She

D   No change

12 In sentence 14, funi should be changed to

A   funy

B   funny

C   funnie

D   No change

13 In sentence 15, I should be changed to

A   He

B   You

C   She

D   No change

14 In sentence 16, Finalily should be changed to

A   Finaly

B   Finally

C   Finalely

D   No change

15 Your friend, should be changed to

A   Your Friend,

B   your Friend,

C   your friend,

D   No change

16 Jessica wants to change the closing of her letter. Which closing is written correctly?

A   love

B   Love

C   Love,

D   love,

GO ON

UNIT 3

Writing Test: Unit 3, continued

WRITTEN COMPOSITION

Directions: Read writing prompts A and B. Choose one to write a composition. Write on separate sheets of paper. Use the Writer's Checklist to make sure that you do your best work.

Prompt A

Sometimes people need to change plans because of bad weather. Write a narrative paragraph about a time you or someone you know needed to change plans because of bad weather.

——————————————— **OR** ———————————————

Prompt B

Many people prepare for emergencies caused by natural forces. For example, you may have practiced fire drills or talked with someone about what to do during a flood or an earthquake. Write a narrative paragraph about ways you have prepared for an emergency caused by natural forces.

Writer's Checklist

Does your composition
- ☑ have a beginning, a middle, and an end?
- ☑ include real events, people, and places?
- ☑ use specific details that let the reader "see and feel" what is happening?
- ☑ express the writer's feelings?

UNIT 3

DONE!

Unit 4: Creepy Classics

Unit Test for Progress Monitoring:
    Reading and Language Test 47
Unit Test for Progress Monitoring: Writing Test 56

Inside Language, Literacy, and Content • Level C

Reading and Language Test: Unit 4

Directions: Read each question and choose the best answer.

1 Which word means "to make something new"?

A apply

B create

C scientist

D successful

2 Which word means "very bad or harmful"?

A evil

B amazed

C creature

D commercial

3 Which word means "very interested in something"?

A lonely

B original

C hideous

D fascinated

4 Which word means "a character that represents an organization"?

A mascot

B scientist

C creature

D experiment

5 Which word means "old but good"?

A actor

B apply

C classic

D successful

6 Which word means "someone in a story"?

A terror

B offstage

C process

D character

7 Which word means "a group of people who watch or listen to something"?

A actor

B audience

C response

D commercial

8 Which word means "to no longer be seen"?

A arrange

B amazed

C disappear

D experiment

9 Which word means "the main message of a story"?

A locate

B theme

C record

D support

10 Which word means "a certain way of expressing an idea"?

A style

B destroy

C specific

D element

11 Which word means "to find out or to show what something is"?

A relate

B discuss

C identify

D narrative

12 Which word means "the way something is organized or put together"?

A report

B explain

C resource

D structure

GO ON

UNIT 4

GRAMMAR & SENTENCE STRUCTURE

Directions: For each question, read the sentences in the box. Then read the question and choose the best answer.

13 | Henry won the bicycle in the contest. He is the luckier person I know.

The word luckier should be changed to

A   luckiest

B   luckyest

C   most lucky

D   No change

14 | We hiked in the Grand Canyon. It was the excitinger thing I have ever done.

The word excitinger should be changed to

A   excitingest

B   more excitinger

C   most exciting

D   No change

15 | The hill was steep. It was dangerouser than we thought.

The word dangerouser should be changed to

A   dangerer

B   more dangerous

C   most dangerous

D   No change

16 | The boy was just learning to swim. He went in the more shallow of the three pools.

The words more shallow should be changed to

A   shallower

B   shallowest

C   most shallow

D   No change

17 | The nurse was helpful. He took good care of my mother in the hospital.

The word helpful should be changed to

A   helpfuler

B   helpfulest

C   more helping

D   No change

18 | The two costumes were very different. However, one was definitely stranger than the other.

The words stranger should be changed to

A   strangest

B   more strange

C   most strange

D   No change

GO ON

UNIT 4

Reading and Language Test: Unit 4, *continued*

19 | The storm was getting stronger. The waves crashed <u>wild</u> on the beach. |

The word <u>wild</u> should be changed to

A   wildly

B   wilder

C   wildest

D   No change

20 | The dancers moved together. They raised their arms <u>graceful</u>. |

The word <u>graceful</u> should be changed to

A   gracefully

B   very graceful

C   more graceful

D   No change

21 | The racers sped <u>lightly and quick</u>. |

The words <u>lightly and quick</u> should be changed to

A   light and quick

B   light and quickly

C   lightly and quickly

D   No change

22 | Wear your always seatbelt. |

How should this sentence be changed?

A   Wear always your seatbelt.

B   Wear seatbelt your always.

C   Always wear your seatbelt.

D   No change

GO ON

UNIT 4

READING COMPREHENSION & LITERARY ANALYSIS

Directions: Questions 23–27 are about "A Walk Downtown." Read the selection.
Then read each question and choose the best answer.

A Walk Downtown

Last Tuesday I was having an <u>unhappy</u> morning at work. I wanted to take a break and relax a bit. I decided to have lunch at a café that is a short walk from my office. But my break was soon anything but relaxing.

As I walked to the café, I found myself beside a young man. He was wearing ripped jeans and an old denim jacket. He was listening to music on an MP3 player. The music was very loud. I could hear it clearly. I could not believe how rude the words to the songs were. To make matters worse, part of the sidewalk was being repaired, so we had to walk very closely to one another.

I slowed down to let him pass by me. As I did this, he seemed to slow down, too. When I sped up, he did the same and was quickly beside me again. I couldn't see his face, but I imagined him smiling at my frustration. I wanted only to be away from him now, so I decided to return to my office.

I stopped at a newspaper stand. I pretended to look at the newspapers. The young man stopped,

too. He began to look through the magazines. Feeling <u>impatient</u>, I immediately turned and quickly walked away. After about twenty seconds, I looked back toward the newsstand. I noticed him heading my way. His pace was fast. I guessed that he would catch up with me before I reached the end of the block.

I had been walking backwards as I watched him coming toward me. Turning around, I was surprised to see an orange barricade just inches in front of me. With no time to stop, I struck the barricade and fell head first into a shallow pit. I landed like a sack of flour on a piece of broken concrete.

When I awoke, I was surprised to find the young man with the ripped jeans kneeling beside me. He was gently tying a bandage around my head. When I looked at him closely, I saw that he had torn a sleeve from his shirt to make the dressing for my wound. My right leg was bent in an odd manner, too. I tried to straighten it. The young man placed his hand on my knee and calmly shook his head.

"You have a deep cut in your leg," he said.

Then I saw that he had propped my leg up on a piece of concrete. I let my head fall back and tried to relax. Turning to one side, I realized that the pillow under my head was the young man's jacket. It was covered in my blood and certainly ruined. I felt ashamed.

"Thank you," was all I could manage to say.

The young man smiled. "You would have done the same for me."

I closed my eyes. In the distance I heard the faint wail of an ambulance's siren.

GO ON

Reading and Language Test: Unit 4, *continued*

23 What does the main character think of the young man at the beginning of the story?

   A He is dull and boring.

   B He is rude and strange.

   C He is cheerful and kind.

   D He is interesting and funny.

24 What is the turning point of the story?

   A The main character wakes up.

   B The main character falls into a pit.

   C The main character hears the ambulance.

   D The main character stops at the newsstand.

25 What does the word unhappy mean in this story?

   A not happy

   B more than happy

   C to be happy again

   D before being happy

26 What causes the main character to change his mind about the young man?

   A He sees that he and the young man read the same things.

   B He realizes that the young man is actually afraid of him.

   C The young man turns his music down.

   D The young man is very kind to him.

27 What does the word impatient mean in the story?

   A not patient

   B too patient

   C patient again

   D wrongly patient

UNIT 4

GO ON

Directions: Questions 28–31 are about "The Hero." Read the selection.
Then read each question and choose the best answer.

The Hero

"Wow!" said Juliana. "That was a great movie."

She and her dad had just seen *Godzilla* in the old movie theatre around the corner from their house. Even though the film was made in 1998, it was not uncommon for the theatre to show older movies that people wanted to see.

She walked closely by her dad as they headed home, just in case he might have been frightened by some of the chilling scenes. Of course, she had not been scared by the monster. Godzilla did not frighten her. So what if he was a giant dragon with huge scales running down his back like spikes? So what if he had sharp teeth like jagged mountains? So what if he could wipe out an entire group of attackers with one fiery breath? He just wasn't *that* scary. OK, so she did close her eyes a few times during the movie. But most of the time she had kept them open. After all, he was just a big lizard.

"You know," said her dad, "that wasn't the first Godzilla movie. There have been lots of Godzilla films made in Japan. Godzilla has fought many enemies."

He searched his memory. "There was *Godzilla vs. Mothra*. Mothra was a female monster. There was *Godzilla vs. King Kong*, the wild gorilla. That movie was about greed. And I remember *Godzilla vs. the Smog Monster*. That movie was about pollution."

He laughed. "In fact, Godzilla is a real hero. After fighting so many tough creatures, he still comes back for more."

"Yeah," said Juliana. "It seems that, even though Godzilla may be fighting too much, at least he is fighting for good causes."

"You're right," her dad nodded. "But the best film was really the first one. It was made in 1954 in Japan. The film we just saw was the story remade by American filmmakers. In the original film, two men wore a Godzilla costume. It weighed more than 220 pounds!"

Juliana was fascinated. How did her dad know so much?

"Can we get the original movie at the video store?" she begged. "I'd like to get to know the *real* Godzilla, the king of the monsters. I think underneath his scary looks, he has a good heart."

"You're right again," her dad said with pride. He was pleased that his daughter could see through a scary look to what really mattered. He smiled to himself. His smile said that he knew his daughter, too, had a good heart.

GO ON

UNIT 4

Reading and Language Test: Unit 4, *continued*

28 What two things are being compared in this story?

   A how Godzilla looks and how he really is

   B how Godzilla is shown in movies and in comic books

   C why adults like movies and why young people do

   D the experience of watching a movie in a theatre and watching a video at home

29 What main theme do "A Walk Downtown" and "The Hero" share?

   A You should be careful about whom you trust.

   B New opportunities may come when least expected.

   C You must never quit fighting for what you believe in.

   D People and creatures who seem scary may actually have good hearts.

30 Both the main character in "A Walk Downtown" and Juliana in "The Hero" learn a lesson about

   A judging others.

   B making friends.

   C finding courage.

   D being thoughtful.

31 What does the word <u>remade</u> mean in this story?

   A not made

   B made badly

   C made before

   D made again

GO ON

Directions: Questions 32–36 are about "The New Kid." Read the selection.
Then read each question and choose the best answer.

The New Kid

Matt sat with his friend Rob on Rob's front porch. The sun was setting. The sky was a brilliant orange. The two of them watched in silence for several moments. Then Rob spoke.

"How are things going at school?" he began. "Are you making friends?"

Matt stared at the ground for a moment. Finally he said, "It's really hard being the new kid. I feel like no one will even talk to me. What do you think I should I do?"

Rob smiled. "It's hard to say what you should do," he replied. "But I do know what you shouldn't do."

"What's that?" Matt asked.

"What I did when I was the new kid," he answered with a laugh. "Two years ago, I transferred to a new school, too. And more than anything else, I wanted to make new friends. But nothing I tried seemed to work. So I came up with a plan. I figured that if I could get the most popular boy in school, Tommy Clark, to be my friend, then all of his friends would be my friends, too. Well, one day when I was in the gym, I saw Tommy arguing with another kid in our class. This kid, Jeremy, was bigger than Tommy. He was yelling at Tommy. It looked like things might get out of control. So I ran over there as fast as I could and

yelled at Jeremy. I told him that if he wanted to pick on someone, he would have to deal with me."

"Did Tommy thank you for saving him?" asked Matt.

"No, he didn't," Rob answered. "He stared at me as if I had lost my mind. Tommy and Jeremy looked at each other and burst out laughing. What I thought was a fight was actually Tommy and his best friend Jeremy practicing a scene for the school play. The story spread fast. It took a long time before the other kids let me forget what a fool I had made of myself." Rob shook his head and sighed. "I tried so hard to make one friend, and I made everyone laugh at me instead."

"But you made friends eventually, didn't you?" Matt asked.

"Oh sure," Rob replied. "Even Tommy and Jeremy became my friends. For an assignment a couple of weeks later, I wrote a story about what I did and why I did it. Then my teacher suggested I read it out loud in our English class. Slowly the other kids started talking to me. Looking back, I think that if I had just been a little more patient, I would have made those friends a lot sooner. Of course, sometimes it's almost <u>impossible</u> to be patient."

Matt laughed. "Boy, that is the truth!"

UNIT 4

GO ON

Reading and Language Test: Unit 4, *continued*

32 What is the turning point in the story that Rob tells?

A He transfers to a new school.

B He makes a plan to make friends.

C He thinks that he breaks up a fight.

D He reads to the other students.

33 What advice would Juliana in "The Hero" most likely give to Matt in "The New Kid"?

A Remember that not everyone needs friends.

B Do not assume that the other kids are mean.

C Your first goal should be to do well in school.

D Real friends will always support you in a fight.

34 How are Matt in "The New Kid" and the main character in "A Walk Downtown" alike?

A They both fear things that they have never tried.

B They both learn a lesson from someone else's actions.

C They both have a friend who gives advice from past experience.

D They both are trying to fit someone else's idea of who they should be.

35 How are Matt in "The New Kid" and the main character in "A Walk Downtown" different?

A Matt learns about patience; the main character learns about kindness.

B Matt needs to make new friends; the main character needs a new job.

C Matt wants to be like other kids; the main character wants to feel different.

D Matt feels defeated at the end; the main character feels ashamed at the end.

36 What does the word impossible mean in this story?

A not possible

B very possible

C possible again

D possible before

READING STRATEGY

Directions: Read question 37. Write your answer on a separate sheet of paper.

37 Michael is reading "The New Kid." As he reads, he wants to visualize the selection. Write to recommend a strategy that you use for visualizing during reading:

1. Explain the strategy.

2. Give an example of how to use it, based on specific information from the selection.

DONE!

UNIT 4

Writing Test: Unit 4

REVISING & EDITING

Directions: Read the composition. It contains errors. Then read each question and choose the best answer.

A Fair Share

(1) Many years ago, a young man named Edward lived in a small village on the edge of a forest. **(2)** One day, he was out hunting with his father. **(3)** In the distance, they heard a strange sound.

(4) Edward's father looked worried. **(5)** "Gosh!" he said. **(6)** "That noise must be coming from Consu. **(7)** We must warn the villagers."

(8) "Who is Consu?" Edward asked.

(9) His father explained, "Many years ago, a very selfish man lived in our village. **(10)** If he needed part of one tree, he cut down many trees. **(11)** If he was hungry, he ate enough food for three people. **(12)** Soon, there were not enough trees in the forest. **(13)** There was not enough food. **(14)** The villagers had to send him away. **(15)** Only a few people have seen him since. **(16)** They say that he has turned into a monster with a giant mouth and a giant stomach that is never filled. **(17)** Wherever he goes, he eats all the trees. **(18)** If he comes to our village, it will be destroyed."

(19) The villagers were frightened. **(20)** Nobody knew what to do. **(21)** That night, Edward made a decision. **(22)** Quietly, <u>he walked</u> into the forest. **(23)** He followed the sound of Consu eating trees.

(24) Edward hid while he watched Consu. **(25)** He waited for him to fall asleep. **(26)** Then he found several hollow logs near where Consu was sleeping. **(27)** Edward quickly filled the logs with rocks and returned to his hiding place. **(28)** "The villagers will think I am so cool!" he thought.

(29) Before long, Consu awoke. **(30)** He was always hungry after a nap. **(31)** He saw the logs and gobbled them down in an instant, rocks and all. **(32)** Along with the rough logs, the smooth, polished stones filled his large stomach.

(33) "Oh, I'm so full," Consu groaned uncomfortably.

(34) "Now you will only be able to take your fair share," Edward told Consu.

(35) After that, Consu never bothered the villagers again.

GO ON

UNIT 4

Writing Test: Unit 4, *continued*

1 Which of these sentences is too informal to match the style of the selection?

   A sentence 4

   B sentence 5

   C sentence 6

   D sentence 7

2 In sentence 22, what is a sharper way to write the underlined words?

   A he went

   B he crept

   C he moved

   D he stepped

3 Which of these sentences does not match the tone and style of the rest of the selection?

   A sentence 2

   B sentence 12

   C sentence 19

   D sentence 28

4 In sentence 32, which word should be replaced to make the language more interesting?

   A large

   B rough

   C smooth

   D polished

GO ON

UNIT 4

Writing Test: Unit 4, *continued*

Directions: Read the composition. It contains errors. Then read each question and choose the best answer.

Teamwork

(1) "Is this a joke"? Paula asked. (2) "How are we supposed to eat with these?"

(3) In front of each girl there was food and water—and some big silverware. (4) The knife and fork were three feet long! (5) Paula picked up the fork by its handle. (6) She tried to swing the other end into her mouth. (7) It was simply too long.

(8) "It's more of a challenging puzzle than a joke", Replied Coach Roberts. (9) "The first player to solve the puzzle will be team captain."

(10) Coach Roberts had decided to invite the Central Middle School girls' basketball team to dinner. (11) Of all the players, Paula and Eva had shown the most talent. (12) But they always seemed to be working against each other.

(13) In fact, the team seemed to be divided in two. (14) When Eva had the ball, she passed it to her friends. (15) When Paula had the ball, she did the same. (16) Coach Roberts tried to get the two groups to work together. (17) But nothing seemed to bring them closer.

(18) Now Eva marched to the table and sat opposite Paula. (19) Suddenily she noticed that Coach Roberts had seated them so that Eva and her friends sat on one side. (20) Paula and her friends sat on the other. (21) It reminded her of two teams facing each other. (22) Happyly, she knew what to do.

(23) "Hey Paula," Eva said. (24) "Put down your knife and fork. (25) I have an idea."

(26) Paula looked at Eva suspiciousily, but did as she asked. (27) Eva picked up her knife and fork. (28) She reached across the table to Paula's plate. (29) Carefulily, she cut a piece of Paula's chicken and placed it on her fork. (30) She held it in front of Paula's mouth. (31) For a moment Paula did nothing. (32) Then she smiled and took a bite from Eva's fork. (33) "nice work, Captain," Paula said, as she picked up her own silverware and reached across to Eva's plate.

GO ON

UNIT 4

5 In sentence 1, <u>joke"? Paula asked</u> should be changed to

A joke? Paula asked"

B joke? Paula "asked"

C joke?" Paula asked

D No change

6 To add richness to sentence 3, <u>big</u> should be changed to

A great

B large

C enormous

D No change

7 To add richness to sentence 8, <u>challenging puzzle</u> should be changed to

A hard puzzle

B mind puzzle

C kind of puzzle

D No change

8 In sentence 8, <u>joke", Replied</u> should be changed to

A joke", replied

B joke," replied

C joke," Replied

D No change

9 To add richness to sentence 18, <u>marched</u> should be changed to

A moved

B walked

C stepped

D No change

10 In sentence 19, <u>Suddenily</u> should be changed to

A Suddenly

B Suddennly

C Suddenyly

D No change

11 In sentence 22, <u>Happyly</u> should be changed to

A Hapily

B Happilly

C Happily

D No change

12 In sentence 24, <u>"Put down</u> should be changed to

A put down

B "put down

C Put "down"

D No change

13 In sentence 26, <u>suspiciousily</u> should be changed to

A suspiciously

B suspicioussly

C suspiciousely

D No change

14 In sentence 29, <u>Carefulily</u> should be changed to

A Carefuly

B Carefully

C Carefulely

D No change

15 To add richness to sentence 32, <u>smiled</u> should be changed to

A flashed a grin

B looked happy

C seemed pleased

D No change

16 In sentence 33, <u>"nice work</u> should be changed to

A Nice work

B "Nice work

C "nice" work

D No change

GO ON

Directions: Read writing prompts A and B. Choose one to write a composition. Write on separate sheets of paper. Use the Writer's Checklist to make sure that you do your best work.

Prompt A

Imagine that you are shopping at a store and you meet your favorite character from a book or movie. Write a short story about spending the day with that character.

---------------- **OR** ----------------

Prompt B

Some problems are more challenging to solve than others. Think of a time when you found a creative way out of a difficult situation. Write a short story about this experience.

Writer's Checklist

Does your story
- ☑ provide background about the setting?
- ☑ have a plot that makes sense and keeps readers' interest?
- ☑ have one or more characters?
- ☑ have dialogue between characters?

DONE!

Unit 5: The Drive to Discover

Unit Test for Progress Monitoring:
Reading and Language Test 62

Unit Test for Progress Monitoring: Writing Test 71

Reading and Language Test: Unit 5

UNIT 5

VOCABULARY

Directions: Read each question and choose the best answer.

1 Which word means "a place that has lots of trees"?

- **A** clue
- **B** loss
- **C** forest
- **D** treasure

2 Which word means "to look for something"?

- **A** search
- **B** prepare
- **C** discover
- **D** remember

3 Which word means "a large area or body of salt water"?

- **A** ocean
- **B** wreck
- **C** alarm
- **D** rainfall

4 Which word means "the set of bones in an animal or a person"?

- **A** artifact
- **B** explorer
- **C** pyramid
- **D** skeleton

5 Which word means "very old"?

- **A** evil
- **B** lonely
- **C** ancient
- **D** successful

6 Which word means "the culture of a specific place, time, or group of people"?

- **A** audience
- **B** civilization
- **C** population
- **D** neighborhood

7 Which word means "someone who studies the way people lived in the past"?

- **A** character
- **B** immigrant
- **C** passenger
- **D** archaeologist

8 Which word means "very well known"?

- **A** original
- **B** famous
- **C** beautiful
- **D** confused

9 Which word means "a piece of information that is true"?

- **A** fact
- **B** statue
- **C** theme
- **D** discovery

10 Which word means "almost the same"?

- **A** angry
- **B** strange
- **C** curious
- **D** similar

11 Which word means "to put things in a certain order"?

- **A** erupt
- **B** record
- **C** prepare
- **D** organize

12 Which word means "the order in which the events happen"?

- **A** power
- **B** sequence
- **C** tradition
- **D** material

GO ON

GRAMMAR & SENTENCE STRUCTURE

Directions: For each question, read the sentences in the box. Then read the question and choose the best answer.

 John's project is due tomorrow. He will need to finish it quickly.

The words will need should be changed to

A   needed

B   needing

C   needded

D   No change

 The storm lasting for several days. I was happy to go outside when the rain finally stopped.

The word lasting should be changed to

A   lasted

B   lastted

C   will last

D   No change

15   Today was my birthday. I will be happy all day long.

The word was should be changed to

A   is

B   am

C   are

D   No change

 Yesterday it started to rain. I take the clothes off the line. I did not want them to get wet.

The word take should be changed to

A   took

B   taked

C   will take

D   No change

 When I was in seventh grade, I have the best track coach. He taught me a lot.

The word have should be changed to

A   had

B   haved

C   having

D   No change

 I told my brother a story before bedtime last night. It was a story about a clown in a circus.

The word telled should be changed to

A   tell

B   told

C   will tell

D   No change

GO ON

UNIT 5

Reading and Language Test: Unit 5, *continued*

19 | Last summer my sister loved to read mystery stories. She <u>went</u> to the library almost every day.

The word <u>went</u> should be changed to

A goes

B goed

C will go

D No change

20 | I <u>playing</u> the piano every day. I usually practice in the afternoon after school.

The word <u>playing</u> should be changed to

A play

B played

C will play

D No change

21 | My dog loves to play fetch. He <u>brought</u> back whatever I throw.

The word <u>brought</u> should be changed to

A brings

B bringed

C bringing

D No change

22 | Our friends just bought another bird. Now they <u>haved</u> seven birds at their house.

The word <u>haved</u> should be changed to

A had

B have

C having

D No change

23 | Kay <u>will visit</u> her cousins three times this past year. She will see them again next year.

The words <u>will visit</u> should be changed to

A visits

B visited

C visiting

D No change

24 | My friend <u>is</u> the captain of our soccer team last year. We will choose a new captain this year.

The word <u>is</u> should be changed to

A are

B was

C were

D No change

GO ON ➤

Reading and Language Test: Unit 5, *continued*

READING COMPREHENSION & LITERARY ANALYSIS

Directions: Questions 25–29 are about "Journey to the Moon." Read the selection. Then read each question and choose the best answer.

Journey to the Moon

Throughout history, people have wanted to make discoveries. During the 1900s, many scientists and explorers wanted to go to the moon. They believed that it would help us learn more about our universe. They began to think of ways to send a person into space. It took many years to find a way to achieve their goal.

An Important First Step

In 1926, an American <u>inventor</u> began doing experiments with rockets. His name was Robert Goddard. He discovered a new kind of rocket fuel. With this new liquid fuel, rockets were more <u>forceful</u>. His first rocket went 41 feet in the air.

A rocket takes off.

But there was a lot more work to do. A rocket had to travel 240 thousand miles to the moon. Still, Goddard's discoveries were very important. He helped other inventors know more about rockets.

The Space Race

In 1961, President John F. Kennedy made an important statement. He told the world that the United States would send a man to the moon. The goal was to do this by 1970. The Soviet Union had the same goal. Both countries wanted to be the first to get to the moon.

People from both countries were getting closer to moon travel. In April 1961, Yuri Gagarin, an astronaut from the Soviet Union, became famous when he circled Earth.

In May 1961, the United States started the *Apollo* program. *Apollo* was the name of the spacecraft used in the missions. The goal of the program was to land a man on the moon and bring him safely back to Earth. Soon, U.S. astronauts began to travel full circle around Earth in spacecrafts.

United States' Missions

The United States completed many Apollo missions. Sometimes the missions were unsuccessful. For example, *Apollo 1* wasn't able to get off the ground. But then in 1968, the *Apollo 7* mission made it into space. This was the first time the United States was able to send astronauts into space safely.

Finally, on July 20, 1969, *Apollo 11* landed on the moon. Neil Armstrong and Buzz Aldrin were the astronauts on that mission. They were the first people to walk on the moon. The United States had finally succeeded. The *Apollo* moon landing was one of the biggest achievements of the twentieth century.

GO ON

Buzz Aldrin leaving the lunar module *Eagle* to set foot on the moon's surface, 1969.

25 What is the topic of the selection?

A the life of an astronaut

B the dangers of space travel

C how people landed on the moon

D what the moon looks like from space

26 The section headings of "Journey to the Moon" help to show that the ideas in the selection are organized by

A cause and effect.

B problem and solution.

C compare and contrast.

D main idea and details.

27 What does the word <u>forceful</u> mean?

A without force

B with less force

C with a lot of force

D with the same force

28 Which sentence states the main idea of the section "The Space Race"?

A He told the world that the United States would send a man to the moon.

B Both countries wanted to be the first to get to the moon.

C *Apollo* was the name of the spacecraft used in the missions.

D Soon, U.S. astronauts began to travel full circle around Earth in spacecrafts.

29 What does the word <u>inventor</u> mean?

A can be invented

B before inventing

C one who invents

D wrongly invents

GO ON

UNIT 5

Directions: Questions 30–34 are about "Penicillin: The Wonder Drug." Read the selection. Then read each question and choose the best answer.

Penicillin: The Wonder Drug

Good and Bad Bacteria

Bacteria live in your nose, your lungs, and your stomach. Most of the bacteria that live in your body are good. They help your body with everything from processing food to blood flow. However, some bacteria can make you very sick. For thousands of years, people searched for ways to fight these bad bacteria. Finally, in 1928, Alexander Fleming stumbled across the solution to the mystery.

Accidental Discovery

Fleming studied different kinds of bacteria in his lab in London, England. To learn more about the bacteria, he made up experiments to test how they would act in different situations. In one experiment, he left some harmful bacteria in a dish to grow for many days. When Fleming checked on his

Sir Alexander Fleming in his laboratory, 1943

experiment, he found a blue-green mold in the dish with the bacteria. The mold wasn't supposed to be in the dish. Fleming thought his experiment was ruined. Looking closer, Fleming found that the mold had killed all of the bacteria around it. Fleming was not the first person to notice that mold killed bacteria. Molds from bread and cheese had been used in folk medicine to treat wounds and diseases. Fleming, however, was the first person to test the mold in experiments.

From Mold Juice to Penicillin

After a lot of hard work, Fleming separated a yellow liquid that killed the bacteria from the mold. He called it "mold juice." In another test, Fleming wanted to see if the mold juice was harmful to animals. He injected some of the juice into healthy rabbits and mice. The animals survived, proving the mold juice was not harmful to animals. Fleming decided to <u>rename</u> the mold juice penicillin from the *Penicillium notatum* mold in which it grew. Fleming wrote a paper about his discovery in 1929. Other scientists did not pay much attention to his discovery. Fleming lost interest in penicillin and began to work on other projects.

Ten years later, Howard Florey and his team of scientists at Oxford University in England took another look at Fleming's paper. Florey's team did one thing Fleming did not do. They injected harmful bacteria into eight mice. All of the mice became sick. Then they injected four of the mice with penicillin. The four mice that received penicillin lived. Florey repeated this experiment many times with more and more mice. The results were always the same. The mice injected with penicillin lived. The other mice did not.

Using Penicillin on People

Florey's next step was to test penicillin on people. From January to June 1941, he gave penicillin to a few sick people. The penicillin did not harm these people and even made some of them better. As soon as Florey noticed that these people looked better, he stopped giving them penicillin. Penicillin was difficult to make, and he could not make it fast enough. Some of the people stayed healthy. Some became sick again. Florey concluded that it wasn't enough to give penicillin until the person seemed better. He needed to give

GO ON

Reading and Language Test: Unit 5, continued

penicillin until all of the harmful bacteria inside the person were gone.

Florey needed a way to make a lot of penicillin. He went to the United States to ask drug companies for help. When the United States entered World War II in December of 1941, drug companies started making a lot of penicillin. It was used to save the lives of U.S. and British soldiers.

Accidental Wonder Drug

Today, penicillin is still saving lives. It helps cure strep throat, pneumonia, and other serious diseases. Fleming's experiments with bacteria in a moldy dish and Florey's research with penicillin

for people gave the world a life-saving medicine. Penicillin really is a wonder drug that was discovered by accident.

People can buy penicillin at a pharmacy.

---

30 Which of these sentences is true about the discovery of penicillin?

  A Florey used penicillin on mice before he tested it on people.

  B During World War II, Fleming found a blue-green mold that killed bacteria.

  C While Florey talked to drug companies, Fleming lost interest in penicillin.

  D Fleming wrote a paper about penicillin after Florey tested the drug on people.

31 Read this sentence from the end of the article.

> Penicillin really is a wonder drug that was discovered by accident.

Which sentence from the article supports this idea?

  A Fleming, however, was the first person to test the mold in experiments.

  B He injected some of the mold juice into healthy rabbits and mice.

  C Some of the people stayed healthy.

  D It helps cure strep throat, pneumonia, and other serious diseases.

32 What does the word <u>rename</u> mean?

  A not name

  B name again

  C wrongly name

  D one who names

33 Florey understood that penicillin could help a lot of people. Which detail supports this idea?

  A He tested the drug on mice.

  B He asked drug companies to make it.

  C He and his team read the paper Fleming wrote.

  D He and his team had a difficult time making the drug.

34 The dates in the article give a clue that the information is organized by

  A order of events.

  B cause and effect.

  C problem and solution.

  D compare and contrast.

GO ON ➡

Directions: Questions 35–39 are about "The Frog and the Locust." Read the selection. Then read each question and choose the best answer.

The Frog and the Locust
A Hopi Folk Tale

One hot summer, the rains never came. The land was cracked and dry. The Earth was thirsty. The small rivers were dry. The large rivers and lakes had grown smaller. Their shores were wide and dusty. Plants everywhere had shriveled up and gone to sleep. The animals were thirsty.

Early one morning, Paqua the frog sat in a small spot of dew. He longed for rain. So he began to sing. He puffed his throat out round and large. He croaked with his deep voice this song again and again.

> Rain, rain, rain.
> Where are you?
> Where do you hide?
> Rain, rain, rain.
> We miss you.
> We need you.
> Rain, rain, rain.
> Come back to the rivers.
> Come back to the lakes.
> Rain, rain, rain.

Not far from Paqua, sat Mahu the locust. He sat in the shade of a shriveled clump of grass. He longed for rain. So he began to sing. He rubbed his wings together. He trilled with his high voice this song.

> The end of summer is near.
> The sun has baked the earth.
> Like a loaf of bread, she grows round and dry.
> She is ready for the feast.
> Where is the rain? Where is the drink?
> The animals are all here. The plants are
>   ready, too.
> The rivers have grown thin.
> The lakes have lost their shape.
> Let the great feast begin!

Where is the rain? Where is the drink?

Mahu, the locust, sings for rain.

Mahu stopped singing. He listened. Then he heard the deep voice of another <u>singer</u>. It was Paqua. He hopped towards the sound. He found Paqua sitting in the small spot of dew. "Why are you singing?" Mahu asked the frog.

"I am singing to the rain. I am telling the rain to come," answered Paqua.

Mahu smiled. "That is funny. I sing to call the rains, too!"

Paqua chuckled. "What is your song?" he asked.

Mahu began to sing his rain song with his high voice. Soon Paqua joined in, singing his rain song with his deep voice. As they sang, they noticed dark clouds forming overhead. They felt a cool breeze on their faces. They sang louder, Mahu in his high, shrill voice, and Paqua in his low, smooth voice. The rains began to fall.

To this day, Paqua the frog and Mahu the

locust are good friends. They have been singing together and bringing the rain. They discovered how working together for the same goal is more powerful than working alone.

Paqua and Mahu sing for rain.

---

35 Mahu stops singing and then hears Paqua's song. Why is the order of these events important?

  A It shows how Mahu finds Paqua.

  B It describes what finally brings the rains.

  C It explains why the two creatures become friends.

  D It explains why Paqua wants to hear the song Mahu sings.

36 What does the word <u>singer</u> mean?

  A can sing

  B sing again

  C full of singing

  D one who sings

37 The time words in "The Frog and the Locust" help to show

  A the sequence of events.

  B when the story was written.

  C where the story takes place.

  D the actions of the characters.

38 Which of these shows the correct order of events in the selection?

  A 1) Mahu sang. 2) The rain came. 3) Paqua sang. 4) The animals grew thirsty.

  B 1) Paqua sang. 2) Mahu found Paqua. 3) They sang together. 4) The rain came.

  C 1) Rivers grew smaller. 2) The rain came. 3) Paqua sang. 4) Mahu found Paqua.

  D 1) Paqua and Mahu sang together. 2) Dark clouds formed. 3) The rain came. 4) The earth was dry.

READING STRATEGY

Directions: Read question 39. Write your answer on a separate sheet of paper.

39 Maxine is reading "The Frog and the Locust." As she reads, she wants to ask questions. Recommend a strategy that you use for asking questions during reading:

  1. Explain the strategy.

  2. Give an example of how to use it, based on specific information from the selection.

DONE!

Writing Test: Unit 5

REVISING & EDITING

Directions: Read the composition. It contains errors. Then read each question and choose the best answer.

Gertrude Bell: Daughter of the Desert

(1) Today, all the deserts in the world have been mapped. **(2)** Did you know that deserts were once a mystery? **(3)** Few people went into these large, empty spaces. **(4)** One woman was not scared of the desert, though.

(5) Gertrude Bell was born in England on July 14, 1868, but she did not stay there long. **(6)** She was one of the best students in her class. **(7)** After college, she began to travel. **(8)** In 1892, she visited her uncle who lived in Persia. **(9)** (Persia is the old name for Iran.) **(10)** Later, she made two trips around the world.

(11) During her travels, Bell studied history. **(12)** She learned how to look at monuments and how to dig for fossils. **(13)** She also learned new languages.

(14) In 1899, she began to travel in the desert. **(15)** The desert is not an easy place for humans to live. **(16)** On many days, there are no clouds in the sky. **(17)** The sun cooks the dry earth. **(18)** Wind causes sandstorms. **(19)** Sand blows into the air. **(20)** The sky becomes dark. **(21)** People cannot see a few feet ahead of them. **(22)** This can also happen during a blizzard in snow country. **(23)** Deserts can be very difficult places to explore. **(24)** But Bell was very brave. **(25)** Her only companions were the guides who led her.

(26) In these deserts, Bell met many different kinds of people. **(27)** She met chieftains, emirs, and sheiks. **(28)** They called her the "daughter of the desert."

(29) Bell's writings and photographs tell about other nations and cultures. **(30)** She took over 7,000 photographs in the desert. **(31)** Many of the places in her pictures are gone now. **(32)** Without her photos, we would know nothing about them. **(33)** Today, digital cameras help preserve photos longer. **(34)** Without her writings, we would not know her thoughts and ideas. **(35)** This important woman helped save history.

GO ON

Writing Test: Unit 5, *continued*

1 Which sentence should be added after sentence 5 to support the ideas in the paragraph?

A   Bell's family was very wealthy.

B   When Bell died, she was 57 years old.

C   Very few people know about Bell's important work.

D   Few women went to college then, but Bell studied at Oxford.

2 Which sentence in paragraph 4 is **not** related to the main idea and should be deleted?

A   sentence 16

B   sentence 18

C   sentence 22

D   sentence 23

3 Which sentence should be added after sentence 27 to support the ideas in the paragraph?

A   She collected fossils to study the past.

B   She wrote letters to her parents at home.

C   People traveled through terrible sandstorms.

D   People recognized that she was remarkable.

4 Which sentence in paragraph 6 is **not** related to the main idea and should be deleted?

A   sentence 29

B   sentence 30

C   sentence 33

D   sentence 34

GO ON

Directions: Read the composition. It contains errors. Then read each question and choose the best answer.

Henry Rawlinson's <u>search for</u> a Language

The Mystery of the clay tablets

(1) Mesopotamia was the name of an area located between two rivers in the Middle East. (2) Many ruins of ancient cities have been found there. (3) When people first <u>explore</u> the ruins, they saw many clay tablets. (4) The clay tablets were like pages from a book but much larger, thicker, and made from hard clay. (5) They had strange marks on them. (6) People were not sure what they were for. (7) They were not sure how they had been made. (8) One person said they were tracks made by birds.

(9) Henry Rawlinson, an English army officer, became curious about the tablets. (10) He believed that the marks might be ancient writing.

The Search For clues

(11) Rawlinson <u>begins</u> to explore the old ruins. (12) He <u>looked</u> at ancient art that had similar markings on it. (13) He <u>study</u> many written languages. (14) He was determined to solve the mystery.

(15) At last, he <u>discover</u> some ancient writing carved in a cliff. (16) The writing was in three different languages. (17) All told the same story. (18) Some of the writing was similar to the writing on the clay tablets. (19) He <u>climbed</u> the cliff to copy the carvings. (20) It was dangerous, and he <u>works</u> a long time. (21) He stopped only when he found a clue.

The Mystery is Solved

(22) Rawlinson looked carefully at his copies of the writings carved in the cliff. (23) He compared the three languages with the marks on the clay tablets. (24) He discovered a link between the writings and the tablets. (25) Finally, he was able to read the writing on some of the clay tablets. (26) The marks on the tablets were an early written language. (27) They told about things like crops, laws, and medicine. (28) Because of Rawlinson's work, today we <u>knows</u> all these things about this ancient society.

GO ON ➡️

5 In the title, <u>search for</u> should be changed to

A   Search for

B   search For

C   Search For

D   No change

6 <u>The Mystery of the clay tablets</u> should be changed to

A   The mystery of the Clay tablets

B   The Mystery of The Clay Tablets

C   The Mystery of the Clay Tablets

D   No change

7 In sentence 3, <u>explore</u> should be changed to

A   explored

B   explorred

C   exploreed

D   No change

8 <u>The Search For clues</u> should be changed to

A   The search for clues

B   The Search For Clues

C   The Search for Clues

D   No change

9 In sentence 11, <u>begins</u> should be changed to

A   begun

B   began

C   is beginning

D   No change

10 In sentence 12, <u>looked</u> should be changed to

A   looks

B   lookt

C   is looking

D   No change

11 In sentence 13, <u>study</u> should be changed to

A   studyed

B   studied

C   studded

D   No change

12 In sentence 15, <u>discover</u> should be changed to

A   discovers

B   discovered

C   is discovering

D   No change

13 In sentence 19, <u>climbed</u> should be changed to

A   climb

B   climbied

C   climbbed

D   No change

14 In sentence 20, <u>works</u> should be changed to

A   worked

B   workied

C   workked

D   No change

15 <u>The Mystery is Solved</u> should be changed to

A   The mystery is solved

B   The Mystery Is Solved

C   The Mystery is solved

D   No change

16 In sentence 28, <u>knows</u> should be changed to

A   know

B   knew

C   are knowing

D   No change

GO ON

Writing Test: Unit 5, continued

WRITTEN COMPOSITION

Directions: Read the writing prompt and write a composition. Write on separate sheets of paper. Use the Writer's Checklist to make sure that you do your best work.

Prompt

Most people believe that some animals are smarter than others. Scientists measure the intelligence of animals, or how smart animals are, by watching how they behave.

Use the information sheet to help you write a report about how animals show their intelligence.

Areas of Study in Animal Intelligence

- **Attention**—Some animals are able to give their attention to one sight or sound, and ignore the other sights and sounds around them. For example, a cat that watches a mouse ignores the swaying of a tree branch nearby.

- **Memory**—Some animals are able to remember information that they have learned. For example, an elephant remembers where a good water hole is located after spending time away from the area.

- **Tool Use**—Some animals use objects to help them with their work. For example, chimpanzees in West Africa sharpen sticks to use as hunting weapons.

- **Problem Solving**—Some animals can solve problems without being trained to do so. For example, a dog finds a treat hidden under a box.

- **Language**—Some animals can be taught to make the sounds of words. For example, a parrot learns to say "Good morning!"

- **Emotion**—Some animals seem to have feelings like humans do. For example, a dog that chases a ball appears to feel great joy as it carries the ball back to its master.

Writer's Checklist

Does your composition

☑ tell about a topic in an interesting way?

☑ have an introduction, a body, and a conclusion?

☑ have a clear central idea?

☑ use facts and details to support the central idea?

Unit 6: Struggle for Freedom

Unit Test for Progress Monitoring:
Reading and Language Test 77
Unit Test for Progress Monitoring: Writing Test 86

Reading and Language Test: Unit 6

VOCABULARY

Directions: Read each question and choose the best answer.

1 Which word means "to help"?

A arrest

B assist

C capture

D hopeful

2 Which word means "money given for helping someone"?

A right

B slave

C reward

D freedom

3 Which word means "to go from one place to another"?

A travel

B define

C organize

D responsibility

4 Which word means "a record of someone's thoughts, feelings, and actions"?

A slave

B journal

C politics

D dictator

5 Which word means "a belief or a view about a topic"?

A system

B opinion

C government

D responsibility

6 Which word means "a person who is in charge of others"?

A law

B arrest

C leader

D organize

7 Which word means "an area that is open to others"?

A slave

B violent

C rescue

D public

8 Which word means "to make a statement against an idea"?

A right

B escape

C protest

D government

9 Which word means "to explain or tell what something means"?

A fact

B interpret

C organize

D interview

10 Which word means "to prove or make clear"?

A topic

B record

C narrative

D demonstrate

11 Which word means "to put things in a certain order"?

A arrange

B explain

C identify

D discover

12 Which word means "the book or other text that you used to gather information"?

A source

B context

C element

D freedom

GO ON

Reading and Language Test: Unit 6, *continued*

GRAMMAR & SENTENCE STRUCTURE

Directions: For each question, read the sentences in the box. Then read the question and choose the best answer.

 13

> Benjamin Franklin was a man of many talents. People admired <u>his</u> greatly.

The word <u>his</u> should be changed to

A   he

B   her

C   him

D   No change

 14

> Freedom of speech is a right in America. We should treasure <u>it</u>.

The word <u>it</u> should be changed to

A   her

B   him

C   them

D   No change

15

> The runners went to the starting line. The crowd cheered for <u>them</u>.

The word <u>them</u> should be changed to

A   it

B   him

C   they

D   No change

 16

> As the boy came closer, he looked familiar to her. She said, "Now, I remember <u>me</u>."

The word <u>me</u> should be changed to

A   we

B   you

C   they

D   No change

 17

> The doctors met to talk about the patient. <u>They</u> idea for a cure was a good one.

The word <u>They</u> should be changed to

A   Ours

B   Their

C   Them

D   No change

 18

> The queen looked very royal in the old photograph. <u>My</u> jewels sparkled in the sunlight.

The word <u>My</u> should be changed to

A   Her

B   Ours

C   Their

D   No change

UNIT 6

GO ON

Reading and Language Test: Unit 6, *continued*

19 | I entered a photo in a contest. I was very excited when <u>her</u> photo won! |

The word <u>her</u> should be changed to

A its

B my

C our

D No change

20 | The girl with the brown hair sits next to me. This is <u>his</u> desk. |

The word <u>his</u> should be changed to

A her

B their

C your

D No change

21 | The <u>Presidents</u> dog is also famous. She even has her own calendar! |

The word <u>Presidents</u> should be changed to

A President's

B Presidents'

C Presidents's

D No change

22 | <u>Writers'</u> words are carefully chosen. Every word must be perfect. |

The word <u>Writers'</u> should be changed to

A Writers

B Writer's

C Writers's

D No change

23 | "Have you seen my book?" "Yes, <u>ours</u> is over there." |

The word <u>ours</u> should be changed to

A its

B hers

C yours

D No change

24 | We both have cats. But your cat is much bigger than <u>its</u>. |

The word <u>its</u> should be changed to

A his

B mine

C yours

D No change

GO ON

READING COMPREHENSION & LITERARY ANALYSIS

Directions: Questions 25–28 are about "Journeys to Freedom." Read the selection. Then read each question and choose the best answer.

Journeys to Freedom

The struggle for freedom is common. It has been a problem for people throughout history. Some examples are the many battles that were fought in the name of freedom. In such battles, leaders often used force to take over countries and their people. The people fought together to free themselves from their enemies. Freedom is not always about battles or taking over a group of people. Individual people or families seek freedom, too.

Seeking Freedom in a New Place

Imagine living in a country that has hard government rules. The government tells you where to live, what job to do, and what to read. Or perhaps you live in a country with little food. You and your family do not have enough to eat. Many people suffer like this. They cannot live happy, healthy lives. Sometimes they can escape. In order to live better, people move to a new country. The new country has an easier government. In the new country, people have enough food to eat.

In the 1800s, over a million people sailed from Ireland to new homes. They left behind a controlling government. Their country was experiencing a famine. This means there was not enough food for all the people. By leaving, they escaped possible starvation. Many of the Irish traveled to the United States. They left behind their familiar homes and ways of life. They were separated from some family members and close friends. In return, they gained more freedom.

Speaking the Language of Freedom

Like the Irish, other people often move to new countries to find freedom. In the new country,

many often have to learn a new language. This is very difficult. Learning a new language is hard work. It takes time and a lot of practice. Most people who move to the United States learn English. It is the most commonly spoken language in the United States. Until people learn the new language, they might have trouble finding good-paying jobs. Although the people are free, it may take time for them to settle comfortably into their new lives.

Terrible Journeys to Freedom

These days, travel to another country is usually simple. You get in a car or climb on a plane. Maybe you go by boat or train. Sometimes, though, travel is more difficult. People who want to be free will make journeys even when they are difficult.

There are many examples of dangerous journeys to freedom. One example is of the East Germans. After World War II, many people wanted to escape East Germany. The East German government did not make life easy. It treated people badly. People wanted to live in West Germany. In West Germany, people had more freedom. Travel was dangerous, however. People had to sneak across the border. The border was carefully watched by guards. People climbed through barbed-wire fences. These are fences with lots of sharp points. People also dug tunnels and swam across rivers. Sometimes they hid themselves inside packages or cars. If the guards found them, their lives would be in danger. Still, people were willing to risk their lives to be free.

Freedom is important. People suffer when they are not free. They will fight to gain their

Reading and Language Test: Unit 6, *continued*

freedom, but sometimes there is no way to fight. Escape is the only answer. In those cases, people leave behind all that is familiar. They sometimes say goodbye to family and loved ones. They travel to a new country. The new country often has a new language and different ways of living. People will risk so much to make their journeys to freedom.

25 What is the main idea of this selection?

  A People fight hard to beat their enemies.

  B Even after people are free, they may struggle.

  C Leaders often use force to rule their countries.

  D The struggle for freedom is difficult, but important.

26 According to the selection, what is one reason that people sometimes leave their home countries?

  A The laws are tough and unfair.

  B They want to learn a new language.

  C They want to see more of the world.

  D The rate of sickness and death is high.

27 What does the word <u>famine</u> mean?

  A a change in the weather

  B a government that is not fair

  C a time when there is not enough food

  D a place where families can live together

28 How does the writer organize ideas in this selection?

  A as questions and answers

  B in the order events occurred

  C as arguments for and against

  D in groups of causes and effects

GO ON

Directions: Questions 29–34 are about "Change for the Inuit." Read the selection. Then read each question and choose the best answer.

Change for the Inuit

Near the North Pole are many miles of land. It is covered with snow and ice. At first glance, we might think it is too cold for anyone to live there. That is not true. The Inuit live in the Arctic lands of the north. These people depend on the cold climate. They have fished and hunted walrus, whale, and seal for hundreds of years.

Thawing ice makes hunting seals more difficult.

Now the Inuit people are worried. The Earth is warming. The ice is melting. Their way of life is threatened. They believe their lands are being destroyed by other people. They are afraid they will no longer be able to live as they have in the past. The Inuit believe they are being treated unfairly. They believe nations that allow harmful gases into the air are taking away their rights.

The Inuit want the rest of the world to know their problems. They hope that when people understand, they will want to help the Inuit. They have chosen someone to represent them in their struggle. Her name is Sheila Watt-Cloutier.

Sheila Watt-Cloutier has spoken to many groups of people about the problems of the Inuit. She tells them how the gases from automobiles hurt the climate. She tells them how the climate change affects the Inuit.

She explains that the Inuit have always depended on fishing and hunting. The seasons always appeared just the same each year. Inuit hunters knew when and where to hunt. They knew how to teach their children to hunt. Now the climate changes quickly from year to year. Ice melts earlier in the spring. Ice forms later in the fall. Each year is different from the one before. Hunters cannot tell when and where it is safe to hunt. Sometimes, people break their legs, or freeze after falling through thin ice.

The animals have also changed. Caribou are grazing animals related to deer. They have been an important food for the Inuit. Because the number of caribou is getting smaller, they are harder to hunt.

Another problem is thawing permafrost. Permafrost is frozen land under the Earth's surface. It used to be hard all the time. Now the houses are falling down because the land is softer and unstable.

As an advocate for the Inuit, Sheila has spoken to human-rights groups in many countries. She hopes to persuade people to change their ways. Perhaps the United States will make laws to reduce the bad gases caused by automobiles.

Many people think that Sheila's work is important. It was suggested that she should win a Nobel Prize. This award is given each year for work that helps people of the world. Because she was suggested for a Nobel Prize, many people learned about her work and the Inuit problems.

Sheila Watt-Cloutier, born in Arctic Canada, speaks to many groups about global warming.

Inside Language Literacy

GO ON ▶

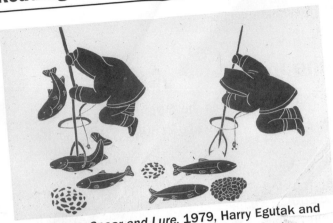

Fishing with Spear and Lure, 1979, Harry Egutak and Mona Ohoveluk. Stencil, Dennos Museum Center, Northwestern Michigan College, Traverse City, Michigan.

The result of Sheila's work is still unclear. Will people stop creating harmful gases? Will people find other solutions to the changing climate? Perhaps the warming will stop. Perhaps the Inuit will learn new ways to hunt. Perhaps the ice will melt completely and the Inuit will move south.

Only time will tell whether or not the Inuit will win their struggle. For now, Sheila will keep talking. And the Inuit will fight for the right to live and hunt on the land they thought they understood.

29 What is the main idea of the selection?

A It is difficult to live in a cold climate.

B Each of us can do something to help the Inuit.

C The Inuit have a problem and want to make it known.

D Groups that are mainly hunters need to change to survive.

30 Why is the change in the weather important?

A The Inuit depend on the cold weather to live.

B The change in the weather is destroying crops.

C The change in the weather is killing too many people.

D The Inuit could live more easily if the weather were warmer.

31 The word caribou means a kind of

A ocean fish.

B melting ice.

C native hunter.

D grazing animal.

32 How does the writer help readers understand the cause of the Inuit's worry?

A She includes examples of the harmful effects.

B She sets up a series of questions and answers.

C She persuades readers by using her own opinions.

D She tells an ancient story that relates to modern times.

33 An advocate is a person who

A travels to many countries.

B depends on cold climates.

C speaks in support of others.

D avoids large groups of people.

34 How are the people in "Change for the Inuit" like the people in "Journeys to Freedom"?

A They both are taking action to defend their rights.

B They both are making dangerous escapes to freedom.

C They both are being forced to leave their home countries.

D They both are learning new languages for their new lives.

GO ON

Directions: Questions 35–40 are about "Failure Is Impossible." Read the selection. Then read each question and choose the best answer.

Failure Is Impossible

In 1872, Susan B. Anthony and several other women were arrested. What was their crime? They were charged with voting in an election. The election was for the President of the United States of America. It is hard to believe that voting was a crime. For women in 1872, it was. Women were not allowed to vote. One brave woman, Susan B. Anthony, would help change this unfair law. Anthony spent most of her life working for women's right to vote.

Susan B. Anthony at eighty, January 1900.

Anthony realized that the Constitution of the United States needed to change in order for women to have the same freedoms as men. The Constitution sets forth broad laws and rights for Americans. Each year, beginning in 1878, Anthony and her supporters urged the United States government to give women national voting rights. Each year the request was refused.

Anthony also worked to educate people about many other legal rights that women needed. These were the same rights given to men. At that time, many things were not equal between men and women. Women were not allowed to practice medicine or law. Most colleges did not accept women. Married women could not own property. Married women could not keep the money they earned.

Anthony knew that women's rights had a long way to go. She gave speeches throughout the country. She talked to people everywhere she traveled. She started a newspaper to discuss women's rights. She and a group of people dedicated to the same cause worked hard for many years.

People did not always agree with them. In fact, most men and women thought that things were just fine the way they were. Anthony and her supporters understood the importance of what they were doing. They kept fighting. Anthony knew they were working for the future of other young women.

In 1906, Anthony spoke at a meeting for voting rights. She was eighty-six years old. She said she was disappointed that women did not yet have the vote. She also said she was hopeful. She believed that people can <u>accomplish</u> great things when they know they are right. She said that, with people as brave and hard working as the people at the meeting, "failure is impossible."

In 1920, the 19th Amendment to the United States Constitution was passed. It gave voting rights to every woman citizen in the United States. Anthony did not live to see this happen. However, her courage and tireless work created the path to freedom—the freedom for women to vote without being arrested.

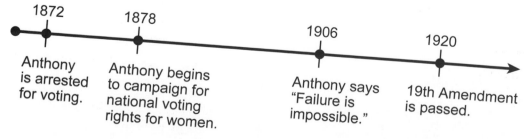

1872	1878	1906	1920
Anthony is arrested for voting.	Anthony begins to campaign for national voting rights for women.	Anthony says "Failure is impossible."	19th Amendment is passed.

Inside Language Literacy

GO ON ▶

UNIT 6

Reading and Language Test: Unit 6, *continued*

35 The main idea of this selection is how

   A the Constitution was written.

   B women used to have limited rights.

   C laws are changed in the United States.

   D one women worked for the right to vote.

36 Based on the selection, what does the title "Failure Is Impossible" mean?

   A When the laws are on your side, you can do anything.

   B When people are brave and right in their beliefs, they will succeed.

   C When people are used to succeeding, they always expect the best result.

   D When everyone is depending on you to do something, you will make it happen.

37 How are the writers of "Failure Is Impossible" and "Journeys to Freedom" similar?

   A They use facts to persuade the reader.

   B They ask questions to get the reader to think.

   C They present opposite points of view to be fair.

   D They make their writing more interesting by including fiction.

38 What does the word <u>accomplish</u> mean?

   A understand or get

   B explain or describe

   C remember or honor

   D complete or achieve

39 How is the topic in "Failure Is Impossible" different from the other reading selections in this unit?

   A It does not have a happy ending.

   B It is mainly about a group of people.

   C It describes events that really happened.

   D It tells only about a time period from the past.

40 What topic do all three reading selections in this unit have in common?

   A saving the land

   B fighting for rights

   C learning new skills

   D leaving for a new place

READING STRATEGY

Directions: Read question 41. Write your answer on a separate sheet of paper.

41 Tomoko is reading "Failure Is Impossible." As she reads, she wants to determine what information is most important. Write to recommend a strategy that you use for determining importance during reading:

   1. Explain the strategy.

   2. Give an example of how to use it, based on specific information from the selection.

UNIT 6

Inside Language, Literacy, and Content • Level C

Writing Test: Unit 6

REVISING & EDITING

Directions: Read the composition. It contains errors. Then read each question and choose the best answer.

Free to Choose a Job

(1) Women today are free to make decisions that affect their lives. (2) They can vote. (3) They can hold government offices. (4) They can choose to do many kinds of work.

(5) Only two hundred years ago, this was not true. (6) Many people believed that women could do only certain kinds of jobs. (7) For example, some people thought it was silly to imagine a woman as a doctor. (8) They thought women did not have the ability or the energy for such important work.

(9) Elizabeth Blackwell was a woman with ability and energy. (10) She told people that she wanted to become a doctor. (11) They told her it was impossible. (12) There were no women students in medical schools.

(13) Blackwell studied medicine anyway. (14) At first, she studied privately. (15) Then she sent letters to more than twelve colleges of medicine. (16) Most of the colleges refused to teach her. (17) The students at Geneva College voted to let her in. (18) They thought that the vote was a joke!

(19) Although some people were unfriendly to her, Blackwell worked hard to learn. (20) Her actions have made it easier for women today to have any job they want. (21) She graduated in 1849 as a top student in her class. (22) That still did not make things easy for her. (23) No one would give her a job as a doctor in New York.

(24) Blackwell went to Paris and learned to treat women and their babies. (25) She returned to New York and joined two other women to open a hospital. (26) She treated poor women and children. (27) She used the hospital as a college to train more women doctors. (28) After that, other colleges began to take women as students of medicine.

(29) Today, women have jobs in medicine, law, government, and many other fields. (30) They can thank people like Elizabeth Blackwell.

GO ON

Writing Test: Unit 6, *continued*

1 Which sentence should be added after sentence 5 to support the ideas in the paragraph?

   A The other students were men.

   B Doctors would not train or hire her.

   C Some of her patients were children.

   D Women could not vote or hold office.

2 Sentence 12 should be moved

   A after sentence 8

   B after sentence 15

   C after sentence 19

   D after sentence 27

3 Which word or words should be added to the beginning of sentence 25 to help connect the ideas?

   A Also,

   B Then,

   C First,

   D After all,

4 Which sentence should be moved to the end of the last paragraph?

   A sentence 9

   B sentence 11

   C sentence 20

   D sentence 26

UNIT 6

GO ON

Inside Language, Literacy, and Content • Level C

Directions: Read the composition. It contains errors. Then read each question and choose the best answer.

Riding for Freedom

(1) In the 1760s, the thirteen British colonyes in North America were growing. (2) In the 1770s, however, colonists became unhappy with the British government. (3) They wanted to be independent. (4) They formed groups to stand up for his freedom. (5) Those who fought for change were known as patriots. (6) The colonists' need for change led to a war between great Britain and America. (7) This war is known as the American revolutionary War (1775-1783).

(8) Many people were important in this fight for freedom. (9) However, two people played key roles as messengers. (10) One was well known: Paul Revere. (11) The other was a quiet hero named Sybil Ludington.

(12) On April 18, 1775, the British Army was going to invade two towns in Massachusetts. (13) Paul Revere heard about this. (14) He rode his horse through the countryside, alerting the townspeople. (15) He warned me that the British Army was coming. (16) When the British arrived, everyone was ready. (17) The batle that followed was the start of the war.

(18) Sybil Ludington also warned colonists about the British Armys attack. (19) On the night of April 26, 1777, the town of Danbury, Connecticut, was the target. (20) The British Army burned it. (21) When Sybils father learned of this, he knew he must bring people together to fight back. (22) He needed a messenger to give it the news.

(23) Ludington was only sixteen years old, but she knew what she had to do. (24) She was a good ridder, but the route was risky. (25) The night was dark and rainy. (26) There were many dangers in the woods. (27) She rode forty miles through the stormy night. (28) She spread the news.

(29) When she returned to her home, more than 400 men had gathered to fight the British. (30) They cheered for her as she rode in. (31) She felt as though she were part of the revolution. (32) She, too, was fighting for freedom.

GO ON

5 In sentence 1, <u>colonyes</u> should be changed to

A   colonys

B   colonies

C   colonyies

D   No change

6 In sentence 4, <u>his</u> should be changed to

A   my

B   her

C   their

D   No change

7 In sentence 6, <u>great Britain and America</u> should be changed to

A   Great Britain and America

B   great Britain and america

C   Great Britain and america

D   No change

8 In sentence 7, <u>American revolutionary War</u> should be changed to

A   american Revolutionary war

B   American revolutionary war

C   American Revolutionary War

D   No change

9 In sentence 9, <u>played</u> should be changed to

A   plaid

B   playd

C   plaied

D   No change

10 In sentence 15, <u>me</u> should be changed to

A   it

B   him

C   them

D   No change

11 In sentence 17, <u>batle</u> should be changed to

A   batel

B   battle

C   battel

D   No change

12 In sentence 18, <u>Armys</u> should be changed to

A   Army's

B   Armies

C   Armies's

D   No change

13 In sentence 20, <u>it</u> should be changed to

A   her

B   him

C   them

D   No change

14 In sentence 21, <u>Sybils</u> should be changed to

A   Sybils'

B   Sybil's

C   Sybils's

D   No change

15 In sentence 22, <u>it</u> should be changed to

A   us

B   him

C   them

D   No change

16 In sentence 24, <u>ridder</u> should be changed to

A   rider

B   rideer

C   ridderr

D   No change

Writing Test: Unit 6, *continued*

WRITTEN COMPOSITION

Directions: Read writing prompts A and B. Choose one to write a composition. Write on separate sheets of paper. Use the Writer's Checklist to make sure that you do your best work.

Prompt A

If you were the mayor of your town or city, what is the first change you would you make? Write a cause-and-effect essay that explains why you would make this change or how the change would affect the people in your community.

--- **OR** ---

Prompt B

Imagine that a new rule has been passed: Students may no longer have cell phones at your school. Write a cause-and-effect essay about why the new rule has been passed and how the students will react to it.

Writer's Checklist

Does your composition

☑ have an introduction with a clear main idea?

☑ have a body that explains the causes and effects in detail?

☑ have a conclusion that sums up the main idea and leaves the reader with something to think about?

DONE!

Unit 7: Star Power

Unit Test for Progress Monitoring:
  Reading and Language Test 92
Unit Test for Progress Monitoring: Writing Test 101

Reading and Language Test: Unit 7

VOCABULARY

Directions: Read each question and choose the best answer.

1 Which word means "to keep going"?

  A orbit

  B reduce

  C continue

  D temperature

2 Which word means "to throw or drop many things over a wide area"?

  A scatter

  B remain

  C migrate

  D telescope

3 Which word means "a story"?

  A tale

  B roam

  C space

  D hunter

4 Which word means "the area between two points"?

  A vary

  B track

  C advice

  D distance

5 Which word means "something that is helpful"?

  A unit

  B benefit

  C universe

  D temperature

6 Which word means "to keep safe"?

  A orbit

  B reduce

  C protect

  D release

7 Which word means "waste that harms nature"?

  A space

  B remain

  C pollution

  D telescope

8 Which word means "the area where plants and animals live and grow"?

  A unit

  B track

  C migrate

  D environment

9 Which word means "correct for the situation"?

  A discuss

  B identify

  C style

  D appropriate

10 Which word means "to break down information into parts to understand it better"?

  A analyze

  B element

  C resource

  D sequence

11 Which word means "to judge the value or worth of something"?

  A fact

  B locate

  C classic

  D evaluate

12 Which word means "to think about how two things are alike and different"?

  A specific

  B category

  C compare

  D structure

UNIT 7

GO ON

Inside Language, Literacy, and Content • Level C

Reading and Language Test: Unit 7, continued

GRAMMAR & SENTENCE STRUCTURE

Directions: For each question, read the sentences in the box. Then read the question and choose the best answer.

13

> My mom could not give me a ride. I took the bus over town to my friend's house.

The word over should be changed to

A   on

B   above

C   across

D   No change

14

> The actor sat beside the writer. They wanted to discuss the meaning of the scene.

The word beside should be changed to

A   into

B   over

C   across

D   No change

15

> We drove on the tunnel. It feels strange to drive under water for so many miles.

The word on should be changed to

A   from

B   above

C   through

D   No change

16

> Roger climbed into the ladder. He went slowly so he would not fall.

The word into should be changed to

A   in

B   down

C   above

D   No change

17

> Anna looked in the fence to the neighbor's yard. There was still no sign of her friends.

The word in should be changed to

A   on

B   over

C   beside

D   No change

18

> They put the puppy above his soft bed. He was tired from playing all day.

The word above should be changed to

A   on

B   over

C   below

D   No change

UNIT 7

Inside Language Literacy

GO ON

Reading and Language Test: Unit 7, *continued*

19 | The river flowed quickly during the storm. Branches and leaves were carried along with <u>you</u>.

The word <u>you</u> should be changed to

A it

B me

C they

D No change

20 | I am very interested in dinosaurs. I want to learn everything I can about <u>him</u>.

The word <u>him</u> should be changed to

A it

B her

C them

D No change

21 | David climbed up the mountain first. The other climbers were far below <u>them</u>.

The word <u>them</u> should be changed to

A her

B him

C they

D No change

22 | I wrote the letter to the school newspaper and signed it with my full name. I wanted them to know it was from <u>me</u>.

The word <u>me</u> should be changed to

A I

B we

C them

D No change

GO ON ▶

Inside Language, Literacy, and Content • Level C

Directions: Questions 23–27 are about "Aim for the Stars." Read the selection.
Then read each question and choose the best answer.

Aim for the Stars

Has anyone ever told you to "aim for the stars"? If so, they want you to set high goals. If you aim for the stars, you can do great things.

The Hubble Space Telescope takes photos in space. Hubble captured this photo of Saturn and one of its moons, Titan.

Today, some Americans complain about space exploration. They say the space program is too expensive. They want to spend the money on other things. I disagree! Space exploration must continue. Our country must aim for the stars!

Why is space exploration so important? For one thing, it leads to new inventions. Today, for example, we use satellites for weather forecasts. Many of the satellites we put into space help broadcast radio waves. Satellites make TV, radio, and cell phones more available. Without the space program, we wouldn't have those satellites. Space scientists have also invented new metals and plastics. They have designed better robots. These inventions are not only used in spaceships. They make our everyday lives on Earth better, too.

The space program helps us become better friends with other countries. The International Space Station is the best example. Astronauts from many lands work side by side on the space station. Countries that used to not get along, like Russia and the United States, now work together for a common goal. As a result, governments get along better.

True, space flight is expensive. Progress in space often seems slow. Still, only about one percent of the federal budget goes to space. (The federal budget is money from the government.) In addition, most of that money is spent here. It creates jobs for thousands of Americans. All in all, that seems like a <u>fair</u> price to pay.

Will space exploration be hugely useful to our country some day? Think about the country's

Astronauts from different countries work together on the International Space Station.

history. The government paid Lewis and Clark to explore and map the country. The government built roads and canals to the frontier. As a result, people moved west. They developed resources there. Our country became wealthy and strong. The same thing could happen in the frontier of space. Many great opportunities surely exist there. Without the space program, we will never find them.

Finally, the space program is exciting. Think about the first landing on the moon. What a lift that gave to our country! Think about the Hubble Space Telescope. This huge telescope has helped us see the universe like never before. It changed the way we view the universe. More than exciting, the space program fills a basic human need. We humans are curious. We want to learn more, see more, and explore more. The space program lets us do that.

GO ON ➤

UNIT 7

Reading and Language Test: Unit 7, continued

Our solar system

Closing down the space program would be like closing down our imaginations. We can't do that. So let's aim for the stars!

---

23 What is the main purpose of this selection?

A   to persuade the reader

B   to describe a problem

C   to entertain with a story

D   to tell how to do something

24 Which meaning of the word <u>fair</u> is used in this selection?

A   carnival

B   acceptable

C   proper or by the rules

D   without showing favor

25 Why does the author compare space exploration to the Lewis and Clark journey?

A   to describe how the explorations were different

B   to give an example of earlier space explorations

C   to show that both explorations had their own dangers

D   to support the idea that space exploration brings opportunities

26 The author believes that the space program

A   costs too much money.

B   does many good things.

C   can be entertaining and exciting.

D   helps friendships within our country.

27 Which detail does the author include to support the idea that the space station is useful?

A   It makes people rich.

B   It keeps travel costs low.

C   It supports broadcasting.

D   It helps governments get along.

GO ON

UNIT 7

Directions: Questions 28–32 are about "Long-tailed Lights." Read the selection.
Then read each question and choose the best answer.

Long-tailed Lights

What would you think if you suddenly saw a new <u>light</u> in the night sky? Would you wonder what it was? Would you be afraid of it? Would you want to learn about it?

People have always wondered about lights in the sky. This is true partly because the lights are so distant. This makes them seem mysterious. Their distance also makes it difficult to learn about them. In ancient times people watched the sky carefully. They wanted to learn about the lights in the sky. People began to notice that some lights appeared suddenly. They had what looked like long tails. These strange lights frightened people.

Today, we understand more about these strange lights. We call them comets. We also call them dirty snowballs. They are actually mountain-sized chunks of dust and ice. Most scientists believe that comets are like scraps of planets. They are made of extra material that was left after the planets were formed.

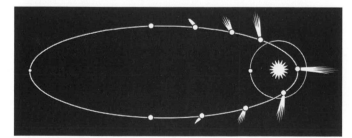

A comet that orbits the sun develops a tail as it nears that giant star.

There are billions of comets in the solar system. Many stay in a cloud of comets called the Oort cloud. Others remain in an area called the Kuiper belt. Only a very few comets break free. Then they move in orbits around the sun. Many comets' orbits are bigger than planets' orbits. This means it takes a long time for a comet to circle the sun and come close to Earth. That's why comets do not seem to appear often.

We also understand today why comets have tails. A comet nears the sun. Then <u>pieces</u> of the comet break away or turn to gas. The gas streams away from the sun. It looks like a tail. Each comet actually has two tails. One tail is made of gas. The other tail is made of dust. These tails can stretch for millions of miles.

How will you feel the next time you see a new light in the night sky? Will you check to see if the light has a tail? If you find a tail on the light, it might be a comet. Then you can look up the comet's name. You can also learn how big its orbit is. If

A long-tailed comet streaks across the sky.

you are lucky, you might even see the same comet later in your lifetime. The next time you won't be so surprised.

GO ON

28 What is the main purpose of this selection?

   A to explain what comets are

   B to tell where comets can be seen

   C to entertain the reader with myths about comets

   D to persuade the reader that comets are important

29 Which meaning of the word <u>light</u> is used in this selection?

   A funny

   B not heavy

   C to make fire

   D a bright glow

30 What effect does the author want this selection to have on readers?

   A to interest readers in traveling in space

   B to make readers afraid of mysterious things

   C to persuade readers to think about ancient times

   D to make readers more curious about the night sky

31 Which meaning of the word <u>pieces</u> is used in this selection?

   A valuable coins

   B parts of a whole

   C written compositions

   D objects used on a game board

32 Why did the author most likely include the last paragraph?

   A to entertain the reader with a funny and imaginary scene

   B to provide the reader with details about the tails of comets

   C to interest the reader by connecting the information to real life

   D to give the reader a better description of what comets look like

UNIT 7

GO ON

Directions: Questions 33–36 are about "Mining the Stars." Read the selection.
Then read each question and choose the best answer.

 **Mining the Stars**

Ryan Petrov was a miner of gems. All day long he would *tap, tap, tap* with his mallet and chisel. He would free each gem from the rocks and hand it to his wife. "This one will be a beauty," he would say. "Please polish it well."

Then she would cut and smooth the stone until it shined. If it was special, Ryan's eyes would sparkle. "We will keep this one," he would say. He would put it in his belt with the others. "We will find something less beautiful to sell."

The stones Petrov and his wife did sell would bring them only a coin or two.

Each night, the Petrovs would eat their thin soup as the stars twinkled above. Ryan was filled by thoughts of his precious gems. Under his mattress, they warmed him like a toasty fire at bedtime. His wife shivered under her thin blanket and dreamed of beef stew.

Each morning, Ryan would take the rare stones from his mattress and place them in his belt for luck.

The couple worked day after day. Ryan continued to sell the less beautiful gems and keep the best. Months passed. The earth had fewer and fewer gems to mine. Fewer coins passed into Ryan's hands. Their soup grew thinner and thinner. Still, Ryan would not sell his best gems. His hunger for jewels was stronger than his hunger for food.

One night he gazed at the stars. His eyes grew wide as he remembered the stories.

"They say the stars are full of giant jewels. That is why they shine so brightly!" he told his wife. "I am the best miner around, but the earth has no more gems. I must climb into the sky!"

"But the skies are dangerous!" she replied. She, too, had heard stories. "People have gotten stuck. The winds can trap you and you will never be free."

Ryan's eyes sparkled. "I am too clever to get stuck. I will return before daylight. I will bring diamonds, rubies, sapphires, and emeralds. These stones will shine with beauty beyond your imagination!"

He pointed to the gems in his belt. "These will be nothing compared to the ones I bring back. When I return, I will sell these jewels. You will have food, blankets, and a new roof."

Then he climbed the sky.

The stars were his stepping stones. He placed a toe here, a knee there. He leaned on one with an elbow. He grasped another with his hand. Higher and higher he rose, looking for the best gems.

There! A star of shining red rubies drew him upward. No, there! He saw an even better one. He supported himself with the ruby star under one shoulder. He reached higher.

It was then that he felt the force.

At first it made him glad. "My stars are good luck! They are helping me reach farther!" He touched his chisel to a dazzling star. Then he tried to raise his mallet. It was frozen in place. He struggled to move his arms and legs.

"I am caught!" he said with fear. No matter how hard he tried, he could not get free.

GO ON ➡

From then on, Ryan could only see his wife from above. He watched her eat her watery soup. He watched her pull her thin blanket under her chin.

His gems, wet with his <u>tears</u>, would shine brightly upon her. But they could not feed her and they could not keep her warm.

---

33 What is the author's purpose in writing the story?

  A to tell how the stars got in the sky

  B to describe the beauty of the night sky

  C to explain a process for doing something

  D to teach a lesson through an entertaining story

34 Ryan loves his gems too much. Which problem does this cause?

  A He does not believe in himself.

  B He cannot make enough money.

  C He cannot learn how to mine gems.

  D He thinks his wife does not love him.

35 Which meaning of the word <u>tears</u> is used in this story?

  A rushing around

  B rips in a piece of cloth

  C splitting something apart

  D drops of liquid caused by crying

36 Ryan is willing to risk everything to find better gems. What detail from the story supports this idea?

  A He uses the stars as stepping stones.

  B He does not listen to his wife's warning.

  C He brings his chisel and mallet to mine the stars.

  D He does not want to sell his most beautiful gems.

READING STRATEGY

Directions: Read question 37. Write your answer on a separate sheet of paper.

37 Alex is reading "Mining the Stars." As he reads, he wants to make inferences. Write to recommend a strategy that you use for making inferences during reading:

  1. Explain the strategy.

  2. Give an example of how to use it, based on specific information from the selection.

DONE!

Writing Test: Unit 7

REVISING & EDITING

Directions: Read the composition. It contains errors. Then read each question and choose the best answer.

Stargazers

(1) For thousands of years, human beings have watched the stars. (2) We do so for many reasons. (3) The stars are beautiful, and they capture our imaginations. (4) Once, before we had tools to help us, we also had practical reasons to watch the stars. (5) A traveler could find out where he or she was by the location of the stars above. (6) However, a cloudy night makes it impossible to see the stars. (7) Throughout history, facts and stories have been combined to explain the power and mystery of the stars.

(8) Groups of stars form giant patterns in the sky. (9) Long ago, people made up stories about these patterns. (10) They are called constellations. (11) You may have seen the biggest one. (12) Orion was thought to be a great hunter. (13) If you look at the stars near Orion's feet, you can see his two dogs. (14) People told exciting stories about the adventures of Orion and his faithful dogs.

(15) Most people have seen the Big Dipper in the night sky. (16) The Big Dipper looks like a scoop that you could use to dip and collect water. (17) The two end stars in the scoop point to Polaris, the North Star. (18) This star is always north of where you are. (19) You can also see the full moon once each month. (20) During the 1800s in the United States, many African Americans escaped slavery. (21) To do this, they had to run away to the North. (22) They used the end stars in the Big Dipper to find their way. (23) They called the Big Dipper the "Drinking Gourd." (24) They even made up a song called "Follow the Drinking Gourd." (25) The stars helped to guide them north to freedom.

(26) Scientists still study the stars. (27) Stars have helped us realize that the universe is larger than we ever imagined.

GO ON

Writing Test: Unit 7, *continued*

1 Which sentence does **not** support the main idea of paragraph 1 and should be deleted?

    A   sentence 2

    B   sentence 3

    C   sentence 5

    D   sentence 6

2 Which sentence should be added after sentence 11?

    A   It is shaped like a man.

    B   The Big Dipper is easy to see.

    C   The sun is actually a star of medium size.

    D   You do not even need a telescope to see it.

3 Which sentence does **not** support the main idea of paragraph 3 and should be deleted?

    A   sentence 16

    B   sentence 18

    C   sentence 19

    D   sentence 22

4 Which sentence should be added after sentence 26?

    A   They think about the history of the Earth.

    B   They take journeys in space to study the Earth.

    C   They write new stories about the constellations.

    D   They continue to learn new things about the stars.

GO ON

Writing Test: Unit 7, *continued*

Directions: Read the composition. It contains errors. Then read each question and choose the best answer.

The Star Queen

(1) Once, a long time ago, a beautiful queen walked the Earth. (2) The people she ruled loved her. (3) She <u>receved</u> from them everything she wanted. (4) <u>She had jewelry rich robes and soft beds.</u> (5) She was also beautiful. (6) She wanted everyone and every thing to praise her beauty.

(7) <u>Only one being, the moon, did not praise her beauty.</u> (8) Every night, the queen watched the moon rise <u>over</u> the sky. (9) The moon never bowed before the queen. (10) The moon simply rose like a large pearl, <u>a pearl the queen could not touch, or hold or wear.</u> (11) Every time the queen saw the moon, she felt jealous. (12) Little did she know that the moon also watched her. (13) Little did she know that the moon grew tired of the queen's vanity and pride.

(14) One night, the queen dressed in her best silks, <u>they're</u> threads so fine that they gleamed, even without light. (15) She put diamonds in her long hair. (16) Finally, she looked <u>on</u> the mirror. (17) She saw a woman more beautiful than the glowing moon. (18) She walked outside to show her beauty.

(19) "I am more beautiful than you all," she shouted to the moon and the stars. (20) "No light in the sky can match my beauty!"

(21) She never thought her foolish words would find an ear. (22) The wind began to howl. (23) The queen tried to run. (24) The wind lifted her up <u>quickly</u>. (25) She floated into the sky. (26) She saw Earth below, like a <u>peice</u> of blue marble.

(27) <u>Gasping for air she heard, the moon speak.</u>

(28) "Since you think you are more beautiful than the stars, you should sit here among <u>her</u>," said the moon. (29) "Stay with <u>I</u>. (30) You are now queen of the sky."

(31) To this day, you can see the queen frozen in the sky. (32) Her name is Cassiopeia.

Writing Test: Unit 7, continued

5 In sentence 3, receved should be changed to

A recieved

B received

C receeved

D No change

6 Sentence 4 should be changed to

A She had jewelry, rich robes and soft beds.

B She had jewelry rich robes, and soft beds.

C She had jewelry, rich robes, and soft beds.

D No change

7 Sentence 7 should be changed to

A Only one being the moon did not praise her beauty.

B Only one being the moon, did not praise her beauty.

C Only one being, the moon did not praise her beauty.

D No change

8 In sentence 8, over should be changed to

A in

B behind

C between

D No change

9 In sentence 10, a pearl the queen could not touch, or hold or wear should be changed to

A a pearl the queen could not touch or hold or wear

B a pearl the queen could not touch or hold, or wear

C a pearl the queen could not touch, hold, or wear

D No change

10 In sentence 14, they're should be changed to

A their

B there

C thare

D No change

11 In sentence 16, on should be changed to

A in

B about

C above

D No change

12 In sentence 24, quickly should be changed to

A qwickly

B qickly

C kwickly

D No change

13 In sentence 26, peice should be changed to

A peas

B piece

C peace

D No change

14 Sentence 27 should be changed to

A Gasping for air she heard the moon speak.

B Gasping for air, she heard the moon speak.

C Gasping, for air she heard the moon speak.

D No change

15 In sentence 28, her should be changed to

A it

B him

C them

D No change

16 In sentence 29, I should be changed to

A me

B her

C him

D No change

UNIT 7

GO ON

Writing Test: Unit 7, continued

Directions: Read writing prompts A and B. Choose one to write a composition. Write on separate sheets of paper. Use the Writer's Checklist to make sure that you do your best work.

Prompt A

Think of a time when you experienced a very heavy rainstorm, a wildly windy day, or a baking hot afternoon. Write a composition that describes what you saw, heard, and felt in such weather.

——————— **OR** ———————

Prompt B

What is your favorite season? Some people enjoy the crispness of fall. Others like the long, warm days of summer. Write a composition that describes your favorite season.

Writer's Checklist

Does your composition

☑ clearly describe a real person, place, or thing?

☑ use vivid words?

☑ include specific details, especially sensory details?

DONE!

UNIT 7

Unit 8: Art and Soul

Unit Test for Progress Monitoring:
   Reading and Language Test 107
Unit Test for Progress Monitoring: Writing Test 116

Reading and Language Test: Unit 8

VOCABULARY

Directions: Read each question and choose the best answer.

1 Which word means "to think something is good or right"?

A collect

B perform

C approve

D decorate

2 Which word means "a contest"?

A career

B concert

C costume

D competition

3 Which word means "to help"?

A carve

B droop

C support

D interpret

4 Which word means "something you play to make music"?

A scientist

B instrument

C experiment

D passenger

5 Which word means "to move along slowly in the air or on water"?

A drift

B mask

C whisper

D discover

6 Which word means "to try hard"?

A carve

B perform

C struggle

D decorate

7 Which word means "strongly affected by something"?

A droop

B design

C useless

D impressed

8 Which word means "to save"?

A proud

B preserve

C interpret

D complain

9 Which word means "to choose"?

A select

B report

C create

D explain

10 Which word means "to share information"?

A identify

B analyze

C resource

D communicate

11 Which word means "a feeling that something is true or right"?

A belief

B discover

C category

D compare

12 Which word means "a group of related things that are put in a certain order"?

A series

B concert

C element

D interview

GO ON ➡

UNIT 8

Reading and Language Test: Unit 8, continued

GRAMMAR & SENTENCE STRUCTURE

Directions: For each question, read the words in the box. Then read the question and choose the best answer.

13

| My friend Maria _____. |

Which answer correctly completes the sentence?

A plays basketball.

B beautiful as she is.

C my friend from school.

D baseball and basketball.

14

| The chef _____. |

Which answer correctly completes the sentence?

A and the best chicken dish I ever tasted.

B when I tasted the best chicken dish ever.

C made the best chicken dish I ever tasted.

D making the best chicken dish I ever tasted.

15

| _____ save money in the bank. |

Which answer correctly completes the sentence?

A Hard to

B My parents

C Working hard to

D When you try to

16

| The painting _____. |

Which answer correctly completes the sentence?

A and my family for a long time.

B belonged to my family for a long time.

C belonging to my family for a long time.

D and the artists in my family for a long time.

17

| I understand her reasons. I'm not sure I could explain them clearly. |

What is the correct way to combine these sentences?

A I understand her reasons but I'm not sure I could explain them clearly.

B I understand her reasons and, I'm not sure I could explain them clearly.

C I understand her reasons, but I'm not sure I could explain them clearly.

D I understand her reasons, or I'm not sure I could explain them clearly.

18

| Juan's teacher says the story is perfect. She wants him to make a few small changes. |

What is the correct way to combine these sentences?

A Juan's teacher says the story is perfect she wants him to make a few small changes.

B Juan's teacher says the story is perfect, and she wants him to make a few small changes.

C Juan's teacher says the story is perfect, or she wants him to make a few small changes.

D Juan's teacher says the story is perfect, but she wants him to make a few small changes.

UNIT 8

GO ON

Reading and Language Test: Unit 8, *continued*

19

> The moon is rising. Wolves are howling in the distance.

What is the correct way to combine these sentences?

A   The moon is rising, wolves are howling in the distance.

B   The moon is rising, or wolves are howling in the distance.

C   The moon is rising, and wolves are howling in the distance.

D   The moon is rising, but wolves are howling in the distance.

20

> Gina liked the painting. It seemed to tell a story.

What is the correct way to combine these sentences?

A   Gina liked the painting after it seemed to tell a story.

B   Gina liked the painting before it seemed to tell a story.

C   Gina liked the painting although it seemed to tell a story.

D   Gina liked the painting because it seemed to tell a story.

21

> We got permission. We didn't really need it.

What is the correct way to combine these sentences?

A   We got permission although we didn't really need it.

B   We got permission because we didn't really need it.

C   We got permission until we didn't really need it.

D   We got permission before we didn't really need it.

22

> I will work on my essay. I need help with some of it.

What is the correct way to combine these sentences?

A   I will work on my essay when I need help with some of it.

B   I will work on my essay after I need help with some of it.

C   I will work on my essay until I need help with some of it.

D   I will work on my essay because I need help with some of it.

GO ON

UNIT 8

Reading and Language Test: Unit 8, *continued*

Directions: Questions 23–28 are about "First Dance." Read the selection.
Then read each question and choose the best answer.

First Dance

Mark walked into the living room carrying a basket of laundry. He set the basket on the couch and sighed. His grandmother was dusting the bookshelves. She looked at him.

"What's the matter, Mark?" she asked. "I know folding the laundry isn't your favorite chore, but it seems like something else is bothering you."

Mark's face turned red. "The school dance is this Friday."

"Why are you concerned about that?" His grandmother asked.

"It's my first dance," he answered. "And I'm worried that everyone will laugh at me."

"Hmm," she replied. "I remember my first dance. I was worried that everyone would laugh at me, too. In fact, I think a few kids did."

"Were you embarrassed?" Mark asked.

"Sure I was, at first," his grandmother replied. "But after a while I noticed that the kids who were laughing weren't dancing at all. I realized that they were even more nervous than I was. This may sound funny, but just knowing that there were other kids there who were as nervous as I was made me relax a lot. And once I started to relax, I noticed something else, too."

"What was that?" Mark asked.

"I noticed that how people dance says a lot about who they are," she replied. "At my first dance, I saw boys who were so nervous they were practically tripping over their own feet. I saw boys who danced around like clowns to hide the fact that they couldn't move in time with the music. I saw girls who wouldn't dance at all because they were afraid of being laughed at. And then I saw your grandfather."

"You met Grandpa at a dance?" Mark asked. "What was he like?"

"He was wonderful," his grandmother replied. She smiled at the memory. "I could tell right away that he was a boy who loved music. He never minded other people watching him. He would always look at me and smile while we were dancing. He really enjoyed dancing. We both felt like we were dancing on a cloud."

"It didn't bother Grandpa that other kids were laughing at him?" Mark asked.

"Not a bit," his grandmother answered. "That night your Grandpa showed me that anyone can feel confident just by being themselves. He danced up a storm. When you feel confident, it doesn't matter what other people think or say about you." She put her hands on Mark's shoulders. "After that first dance, I learned to be a lot less shy around people. I felt a lot more comfortable saying what I believed, too."

"I never would have guessed that you once had trouble speaking your mind," Mark replied, grinning. "If you learned so much at your first dance, then maybe I shouldn't be afraid to go to the dance after all."

Mark's grandmother nodded her head. "I think you are going to have a wonderful time. Just have fun dancing. Have fun being yourself."

GO ON

23 The title "First Dance" refers to

   A the first time someone took dance lessons.

   B the first time someone fell in love at a dance.

   C a dance that happened at a school for the first time.

   D a dance about to happen and a dance from the past.

24 What conclusion can be made about Mark's grandmother?

   A She is an excellent dancer.

   B She says what she believes.

   C She is difficult to get along with.

   D She has trouble with her memory.

25 The paragraphs separate the story into parts that help show

   A which character is speaking.

   B the steps of a popular dance.

   C the grandmother's list of chores.

   D Mark's memories of his grandfather.

26 What does tripping over their own feet tell about the boys at the dance?

   A They were fast.

   B They were clumsy.

   C They were dangerous.

   D They were good at sports.

27 What will most likely happen next?

   A Mark will decide not to go to the dance.

   B Mark will relax and have fun at the dance.

   C Mark's grandmother will go with him to the dance.

   D Mark's grandmother will not let him go to the dance.

28 Mark's grandmother says, "We both felt like we were dancing on a cloud." This sentence means that they felt

   A curious.

   B nervous.

   C awkward.

   D delighted.

GO ON

Reading and Language Test: Unit 8, *continued*

Directions: Questions 29–31 are about "Granddad's Paintings." Read the selection. Then read each question and choose the best answer.

Granddad's Paintings

Ben liked to work with his grandfather in the garage. Ben helped his grandfather by getting tools such as hammers or wrenches. It seemed that his grandfather was always working on a project.

Ben and his grandfather decided to build a basketball hoop. With help, Ben used a saw to cut out a backboard. Then they painted it green. The hoop was ready to be attached.

"I need to fasten this well," Granddad said. "Please find some two-inch screws."

Ben looked for screws. He spotted a dusty box of paintings under his grandfather's workbench.

"Did you know there's a box of paintings down here?" Ben asked.

Ben's grandfather looked under the workbench.

"I painted those old things when I worked on the railroad," his grandfather said.

Ben pulled one of the paintings from the box. What a wonderful find! His grandfather dusted it off. The painting was of a big, red train engine.

"What a cool engine!" Ben said. His grandfather smiled.

"I used to love to watch the trains when I was a boy," Granddad said. "The trains were like rockets on the tracks. They sounded like mighty animals as they glided on the tracks and blew their whistles. I knew then that I wanted to work on trains when I grew up."

Ben took all the paintings from the box. He and his grandfather dusted them all off. One by one they hung them up on the wall. Ben spent a long time looking at them.

"What was your job?" Ben asked.

"I built and fixed engines in a giant shop. The trains could pull right in!"

"How did you learn how the engines worked?" Ben asked.

"When I started, I was wet behind the ears," Granddad said. "I did not know anything yet. I started helping workers who knew more than me, just like you help me."

Ben's favorite painting showed a diesel train engine. Ben thought that it must take a lot of teamwork to build an engine.

Ben thought about his basketball team. They worked together like the workers who built the engines in the paintings.

"I have an idea," Granddad told Ben. "You could make a painting about something that you like. I'll be your helper."

Ben thought about what he liked the most. It was definitely basketball. Granddad could help him tell his story!

GO ON ➡️

UNIT 8

Reading and Language Test: Unit 8, continued

29 What does Ben learn from talking with Granddad?

A how to work as a team

B how to play basketball

C how to grow old happily

D how to repair train engines

30 What does the phrase <u>I was wet behind the ears</u> tell about Granddad?

A He had a lot to learn.

B He did not want to work.

C He was always in a hurry.

D He was not a good listener.

31 How are the plots of "First Dance" and "Granddad's Paintings" similar?

A A grandchild worries about a grandparent.

B A grandparent teaches a grandchild a lesson.

C A grandchild remembers a favorite grandparent.

D A grandparent feels sad that a grandchild is growing up.

UNIT 8

GO ON

Reading and Language Test: Unit 8, *continued*

Directions: Questions 32–38 are about "Whirligig Artist." Read the selection.
Then read each question and choose the best answer.

Whirligig Artist

Have you ever seen a whirligig? Usually, it's a brightly-colored wooden bird or human figure. It is attached to a pole, and it has a propeller. Even a little breeze makes the figure's wings or arms twirl.

A large whirligig on Vollis Simpson's farm

Whirligigs have a long history. They were invented in Asia. During the Middle Ages, whirligigs appeared in Europe as children's toys. Later, American farmers made whirligigs that were about one or two feet long. They used them to scare birds away from their crops.

Today, whirligigs are still used as decorations. One man in particular has turned making them into an art form. His name is Vollis Simpson. If you visit his farm in Lucama, North Carolina,

you'll see dozens of them. Simpson's homemade whirligigs are huge. Some stand fifty feet tall! When the wind blows, Simpson's farm comes alive. One of the machines has two mules pulling a wagon. The wind makes the mules kick and the wagon wheels turn. Another whirligig revolves like a Ferris wheel, and it is almost as big.

Simpson's interest in whirligigs was practical at first. As a young man, his first whirligig ran a washing machine. Another one powered his heating system. At that time, his job was to repair farm equipment.

When Simpson retired in 1985, he had lots of spare time. He also had lots of spare machine parts. Why not put them to good use? He didn't have to be practical now. So, he began making the most unusual and colorful whirligigs in the world. Each one explored his love of movement and color in a new way.

Simpson took an old craft to a new level. He cut his figures from steel. He welded on gears and axles. He painted the whirligigs wild colors. Then he studded them with reflectors. That way, the headlights of passing cars made them shine.

Simpson's yard slowly filled with his handiwork. People began to stop. Everyone wanted to see the amazing whirligigs. The word spread. In 1996, officials asked him to show the machines at the Olympics in Atlanta. The crowds were amazed. Soon museums wanted the whirligigs, too. One museum called Simpson a "visionary artist."

Today, Vollis Simpson is a full-time whirligig artist. Most days, he's working on a new whirligig. He's busy. But if you do visit, he'll be glad to show you his latest creations.

UNIT 8

GO ON ➡

Reading and Language Test: Unit 8, continued

32 How does the paragraph structure help the reader understand this selection?

A   by showing steps in a process

B   by separating the information into topics

C   by helping the reader to skim for information

D   by helping the reader read one sentence at a time

33 Which conclusion can be made about why Simpson is successful?

A   He knows how to convince people to buy his artwork.

B   He limits the amount of time he spends on one whirligig.

C   He has a good imagination and knows how to build machines.

D   He has money to support his art and a farm that is easy to find.

34 What does the phrase Simpson's farm comes alive tell about the farm?

A   Animals are born on the farm.

B   The farm crops begin to grow.

C   The people on the farm are very active.

D   A lot of things on the farm begin to move.

35 How does the photograph of the whirligig help the reader?

A   It shows the steps to building a whirligig.

B   It shows details about the parts of a whirligig.

C   It shows the movement of the whirligig.

D   It shows whirligigs from other countries.

36 How are Simpson and Granddad in "Granddad's Paintings" similar?

A   They are both famous.

B   They are both farmers.

C   They both have a talent for art.

D   They both care for their grandchildren.

37 Which theme is found in all three reading selections?

A   Work hard.

B   Be yourself.

C   Stay healthy.

D   Save money.

38 How are the authors' approaches similar in all three reading selections?

A   The authors use questions and answers to get the readers to think.

B   The authors highlight the good things about the people in the selections.

C   The authors include ideas and words of experts to support their writing.

D   The authors use strong words to persuade the readers to change their minds.

READING STRATEGY

Directions: Read question 39. Write your answer on a separate sheet of paper.

39 Max is reading "Whirligig Artist." As he reads, he wants to synthesize information. Write to recommend a strategy that you use for synthesizing information during reading:

1.   Explain the strategy.

2.   Give an example of how to use it, based on specific information from the selection.

DONE!

UNIT 8

Writing Test: Unit 8

Directions: Read the composition. It contains errors. Then read each question
and choose the best answer.

The Heart of a Poet

(1) Maya Angelou is a great poet because she writes from the heart.
(2) Much of her writing is about lessons she learned as a child.

(3) Angelou's early years were not easy. (4) She used her experiences
in her writing. (5) Her parents divorced when she was three years old.
(6) Angelou and her brother moved all over the country. (7) She was
mostly raised by her grandmother in Arkansas.

(8) When Angelou was eight years old, she stopped talking. (9) She
thought that bad things happened when she spoke. (10) She read many
poems. (11) She especially loved poems by Rudyard Kipling and
Langston Hughes.

(12) Angelou finally decided to speak again when she was thirteen
years old. (13) A good friend, Mrs. Flowers, told her to read poetry out
loud because it sounds so beautiful. (14) Angelou said that Mrs. Flowers
helped her find her voice again.

(15) Angelou moved to California when she was a teenager. (16) She
had a problem there. (17) She ended up living in a junkyard. (18) Other
homeless children and teens lived in the junkyard. (19) Angelou spent a
whole month there. (20) She finally took a bus to her mother's house in
San Francisco. (21) She stayed in the city for a number of years.

(22) Angelou has done many different things in her life. (23) She was
an actress and a dancer. (24) She was a streetcar conductor. (25) When
she was older, Angelou became a published author and a poet. (26) As a
child, she found her voice in poetry.

(27) Angelou has had many experiences to write about. (28) Her first
book is called *I Know Why the Caged Bird Sings*. (29) It is about her
childhood. (30) She also wrote four other books about her life. (31) Maya
Angelou is a natural storyteller.

GO ON ➡

UNIT 8

Writing Test: Unit 8, continued

1 Which sentence should be removed from paragraph 2 because it repeats information from earlier in the selection?

    A   sentence 4

    B   sentence 5

    C   sentence 6

    D   sentence 7

2 Which sentence in paragraph 5 needs more specific detail?

    A   sentence 15

    B   sentence 16

    C   sentence 17

    D   sentence 18

3 Which sentence should be removed from paragraph 6 because it repeats information from earlier in the selection?

    A   sentence 22

    B   sentence 23

    C   sentence 24

    D   sentence 26

4 Which sentence **best** fits after sentence 30?

    A   People are surprised that she was once a professional dancer.

    B   When she was younger, she wrote song lyrics as well as poetry.

    C   Many people think her writing is very important.

    D   Presidents Ford and Carter invited her to be on different committees.

UNIT 8

GO ON

Writing Test: Unit 8, *continued*

Directions: Read the composition. It contains errors. Then read each question and choose the best answer.

Julia Morgan: Architect as Artist

(1) Art is all around us. (2) We see paintings and movies. (3) We listen to music. (4) Buildings can be seen as works of art, too. (5) The people who draw designs for buildings are called architects. (6) One architect who became famous was Julia Morgan.

(7) Morgan was born in San Francisco in 1872. (8) She was the first woman to study architecture. (9) She studied at the famous *École des Beaux Arts* in Paris. (10) She started her own business in California with very talented people. (11) They worked together to create many buildings that are still admired today.

(12) Morgan new that buildings can have a great effect on people. (13) Her many prodgects included homes, churches, schools, and even a zoo.

(14) Morgan thought carefully about each building. (15) She had a clear understanding of each owner's personality. (16) This helped her designs.

(17) Morgan's most famous building was the hearst Castle in California. (18) William Randolph Hearst was the wealthy owner of the property, he wanted Morgan to design a beautiful castle with guest houses.

(19) Morgan worked on the property for many years. (20) The design was difficult. (21) Mr. Hearst brought parts from European castles for Morgan to put into his castle. (22) She worked hard to make the buildings fit with each other and the land. (23) Being careful about every detail. (24) Her nowledge of the man and the land paid off. (25) A famous historian once stated, "Hearst Castle is a palace in every sense of the word."

(26) Julia Morgan's work helped people see architecture as art. (27) As splendid as a fine painting. (28) In 1929, she won a special award for being an architect whose works were said to "bring pleasure to the eye and peace to the mind." (29) Julia worked until her death shortly before valentine's day in February of 1957.

GO ON

Writing Test: Unit 8, continued

5 Sentences 2 and 3 should be combined as

A We see paintings and movies, we listen to music.

B We see paintings and movies, Or we listen to music.

C We see paintings and movies, But we listen to music.

D We see paintings and movies, and we listen to music.

6 In sentence 12, new should be changed to

A pnew

B knew

C wnew

D No change

7 In sentence 13, prodgects should be changed to

A projects

B progects

C prodjects

D No change

8 In sentence 14, carefully should be changed to

A carefuly

B carefulily

C carefulely

D No change

9 In sentence 17, hearst Castle should be changed to

A Hearst Castle

B Hearst castle

C hearst castle

D No change

10 In sentence 18, property, he should be changed to

A property, and he

B property, or he

C property, but he

D No change

11 In sentence 21, European castles should be changed to

A european castles

B european Castles

C European Castles

D No change

12 In sentence 23, Being careful about every detail. should be changed to

A She was careful. About every detail.

B Being careful and about every detail.

C She was careful about every detail.

D No change

13 In sentence 24, nowledge should be changed to

A nowlidge

B knowledge

C knowlidge

D No change

14 In sentence 27, As splendid as a fine painting. should be changed to

A Splendid as a fine painting.

B Architecture, paintings, music, and movies.

C Architecture could be as splendid as a fine painting.

D No change

15 In sentence 28, "bring pleasure to the eye and peace to the mind." should be changed to

A bring pleasure to the eye and peace to the mind.

B Bring pleasure to the eye and peace to the mind.

C "bring pleasure to the eye and peace to the mind"

D No change

16 In sentence 29, valentine's day should be changed to

A Valentine's day

B valentine's Day

C Valentine's Day

D No change

GO ON ➡

Writing Test: Unit 8, *continued*

Directions: Read writing prompts A and B. Choose one to write a composition. Write on separate sheets of paper. Use the Writer's Checklist to make sure that you do your best work.

Prompt A

Think of a story you have read that has a strong message or theme. Write a literary response about the story's message or theme. Explain how the theme made you feel. Use details from the story to support your response.

———————— **OR** ————————

Prompt B

Think of a story you have read that has characters you felt strongly about. Write a composition about one of the characters in this story. Explain why you liked or disliked the character.

Writer's Checklist

Does your composition tell

- ☑ the name of the work and the author?
- ☑ what the work is mostly about?
- ☑ how you feel about the work and why?
- ☑ something important you learned from the work?

DONE!

UNIT 8